SUNNY INTERVALS & SHOWERS

By the same author

NON-FICTION

The Essential Guide to London
The Absolutely Essential Guide to London
The Streets of London
Junk
The Antique Collector's Guide
A Scientist's Odyssey (with Professor Hans Kalmus)
Uncle Ernie's System

SUNNY INTERVALS & SHOWERS

Our Changing Weather

DAVID BENEDICTUS

Weidenfeld and Nicolson
London

First published in Great Britain in 1992 by
George Weidenfeld & Nicolson,
91 Clapham High Street, London SW4 7TA

Copyright © David Benedictus 1992

British Library Cataloguing in Publication Data
(available on request)

Photoset by Deltatype Ltd, Ellesmere Port, Cheshire
Printed and bound in Great Britain by
Butler & Tanner Ltd
Frome and Somerset

Contents

All temperatures throughout this book are given in Centigrade/Celsius, except where the context requires otherwise. A chart relating Centigrade to Fahrenheit and knots to miles per hour will be found in Appendices I and II. I generally use inches rather than centimetres, but metres rather than feet; and if this seems illogical I can only answer that the compromise seems to be the most easily understood.

Illustrations

Frost fairs have not occurred this century. Effluent from factories and power stations is more to blame than alleged global warming

The drought at Church Stretton, Salop, 1976 (*National Water Council*)

Hoaxers, hedgehogs, dust devils or aliens from outer space? Artistic certainly (*Calyx Photo Services and F. C. Taylor*)

'For the man sound in body and serene of mind there is no such thing as bad weather; every sky has its beauty, and storms which whip the blood do but make it pulse more vigorously.'

George Gissing (1903)

. . . .

The Wind Bloweth Where it Listeth

'The Westerly Wind asserting his sway from the south-west quarter is often like a monarch gone mad, driving forth with wild imprecations the most faithful of his courtiers to shipwreck, disaster and death.'

Joseph Conrad (1906)

✻

'It will be very breezy up through the Channel'

BBC Weather Forecast (15 October 1987)

We live in a quiet, tree-lined street, in a quiet tree-lined suburb. We are part of a Neighbourhood Watch scheme, but the neighbours grew bored of watching. Recently, and, I thought, appropriately, sleeping policemen were laid in the adjoining streets. Myself, I welcome a bit of action, and on the night of 15 October 1987, I was rewarded with plenty.

Not that dates mean much. I often wonder how many of the dates we do remember are accurate. And why should we remember them? Battle of Hastings, 1066, Columbus, 1492, Guy Fawkes, 5 November, the Great Fire of London, 1666. How strange that the last battle lost by the British, the setting sail of the son of a Genoese weaver to discover a continent, which, according to Thurber, had been discovered many times before – 'but it had been hushed up' – the failed attempt to blow up Parliament, and the burning down of much of our capital city, should be the dates which most of us readily remember.

Of course you remember 15 October 1987. It was the night of the Freak Hurricane, the Killer Storm, the Weather Explosion,

Nature's Blitz. It was the night of the Headline Writer's Benefit. I remember it vividly. It had been breezy, nothing more, and then after the main BBC news, on came the familiar but depressing face of Michael Fish.

'Earlier on today, apparently,' he said, 'a woman rang the BBC and said that she heard that there was a hurricane on the way. Well, if you are watching, don't worry; there isn't.'

The woman's name is Anita Hart, and she worked for a West End firm of solicitors. Asking her son, Gaon, for a guide as to the likely conditions for a weekend in the country, Gaon consulted his charts and identified a depression, which was intensifying alarmingly in the Channel. It seemed to be making directly for the south of England. He told Anita, and Anita asked her secretary to check with the weather man.

On the late night BBC2 weather summary Bill Giles delightfully commented: 'It looks as though most of the strong winds will stay away, although it's still going to be very breezy up through the Channel,' in what was officially called 'deliberate understatement'. The first reference to 'severe gales' was not broadcast until 12.20 am on the Radio Four *Weather Bulletin*.

I am a midnight worker. I watch rubbish on television until I find myself dozing, then I climb the wooden stairs to Bedfordshire, but settle instead for an hour or two at the Apple Macintosh. On that particular night the wind grew more and more vicious. In the wildest gusts there were three distinct sounds. The rushing sound, the moaning sound, and a third sound which I had never heard before and hope never again to hear – a sucking sound. Funneling up Oxford Road, it was gathering speed as it came and it sucked everything up with it. I woke eight-year-old Chloe, who slept on a bunk bed and could see straight out of the window. 'This is quite something,' I told her.

She smiled, and grunted. My wife, looking out of the back window, saw the row of fine lime trees in Kings Road being horizontally stretched, until one of them was uprooted. It landed on our garage. I watched bemused and fascinated, with the guilty thrill of someone who knows that a tragedy is imminent, and who feels privileged to be a witness to it.

I woke early and switched on the radio. There had been a power cut but I could receive London Broadcasting Station News on the tranny. Reports were sparse and inconsistent, but it was clear that the storm had cut a swathe across the south of the country, and that people had died. The full extent of the storm's fury was only apparent to me when I set off to drive to my office in Kingston. Most of our glorious limes had been uprooted. Most of the roads were blocked. Many cars were crushed. There were few pedestrians, and those I saw were grinning a secret and rather fey kind of grin. We were a freemasonry. Anyone of us might have been a looter.

The Local Council were quick to act. By that same evening the angry humming of chain-saws was audible whichever way you turned, and we foregathered in front of the corpses of the trees, comparing notes. People took photographs and brought one another coffee. There was no arguing with our shattered garage and we were amongst the top dogs.

The Royal Meteorological Society's booklet – Volume 43 Number 3 – makes interesting reading. It is a special issue dedicated to The Storm. It deals in great detail with the forecasting of the storm, the damage caused by the storm, a historical perspective, with the massive scholarship that you would expect from such an august body. It frequently refers us to the famous storm of 7 and 8 December 1703 (on the modern calendar) in which the most notable victim, the Bishop of Bath and Wells, was crushed to death.

How fierce was that storm? Such measuring instruments as existed in 1703 suggested that the maximum wind speed then may have been about 150 knots over the North Sea. In 1987 the best that could be reliably recorded was a gust of 106 knots at Gorleston, but then the report turned out not to be so reliable after all, because the anemometer was discovered to have been vandalized a month before the great storm, and was over-recording by about 20 per cent. A hundred knots at Shoreham-

3

by-Sea is therefore regarded as the highest recorded wind speed in the UK, although France provided a confirmed gust of 119 knots (or 137 mph) at Pointe du Raz on the coast of Normandy.

Just as 100 degrees centigrade seems to be the British sticking point for heat (see Chapter 6), so 100 knots is the ultimate these days for gusting winds. According to the Beaufort Scale a hurricane is Force 12, that is to say more than 64 knots (73 mph). The highest recorded gust of all time appears to be 371 kph (231 mph) at Mount Washington, USA.

The storm of 15 and 16 October 1987 was exceptional, but not so much for the strength of the winds. Such extremes might be expected every fifty years or so, although some of the gusts were prolonged to a minute or more, which is decidedly unusual. Remarkable swings in barometric pressure were recorded. At an oil platform off the coast of Norfolk there was a fall of 6.8 millibars in three hours. Between four and five in the morning pressure rose by eleven millibars at Southampton and by 12.2 at Hurn, while the temperature fell by six degrees. Around London the atmospheric pressure fell to 958.5 millibars corrected to mean sea level and recorded near Reading at five in the morning, the lowest level recorded in Britain since an astonishing 925.6 millibars in January 1884 at Ochertyre, near Crieff, Tayside. A low of between 915 and 916 millibars was noticed between Iceland and Greenland on 15 December 1986.

Temperature rises in advance of the storm were astonishing. At Mortimer, to the south of Reading, the temperature rose eight degrees in twenty minutes. What the anemometers recorded was interesting; what the barometers and thermometers recorded was unprecedented.

Numerous flashes of lightning were reported, but very little thunder. The explanation suggested is that the flashes were not lightning at all but power cables colliding in the high winds. Much of the electricity supply over the south of England had been disrupted between 3 am and 9.30 am, which added to the problems of the Meteorological Office. (It is important to emphasize that had the storm occurred over Northern Ireland or the north and west of Scotland, there would have been little media attention. But there would also have been few, if any, fatalities.) It is ironic that many of the anemometers in the south of England were electrically powered and rendered useless when they were most needed, while the wind-recorder on the top of the British Telecom Tower was blown away.

There can be little doubt that the storm of 1703 was the more severe. We do not know how many died. Defoe suggests 103 in London and some 8,000 in the country at large. We do know that whirlwinds and tornadoes associated with the depression occurred in England and Holland. A ship moored at Whitstable was lifted into the air and blown 250 metres inland. The Eddystone Lighthouse, built just five years previously, was completely destroyed along with Henry Winstanley who had designed it. Countless ships foundered and the people of Deal had a grand time looting the wrecks, although the mayor, I am glad to say, did his best to succour the victims, and condemn the law-breakers. Church towers and steeples beyond counting were blown down, and more than 400 windmills. Daniel Defoe did us all a service by recording 'nothing but what may assist in convincing Posterity that this was the most violent Tempest the World ever saw'. He went to Kent to count the fallen trees but gave up upon reaching 17,000.

He describes the City of London: 'As soon as people could put their heads out of the doors . . . everybody expected the destruction . . . yet I question very much if anybody believed the hundredth part of what they saw . . . The streets lay covered with tiles and slates . . . and the houses were so universally stripped that all the tiles in fifty miles round would be able to repair but one small part of it.' He reports the sad case of 'an honest yeoman, being upon a ladder to save his hovel, was blown off, and fell upon his plough, died outright, and never spoke a word more.'

Defoe himself barely survived the storm when a part of a house fell into the street, and only narrowly missed him. 'I draw only this conclusion,' he writes disappointingly, 'that the winds are a part of the Works of God by Nature.'

The effects of the 1987 storm have still not been completely assessed. An estimated three million houses were damaged. The London Underground system, the Old Bailey, the Tower of London and the Stock Exchange were closed down.

Fifteen million trees were blown over, more in a single night than were destroyed by Dutch Elm Disease in a decade, and many others so weakened at their roots that they were to come down in the subsequent storms of 1990. But benign conditions had been experienced for so long that many of these trees may have outlived their natural life expectancy. There had been a substantial campaign to preserve trees, but very little knowledgeable pruning of them, so that many of the doomed trees were top-heavy.

A third of the trees at Kew Gardens came down, many of them several hundreds of years old. At Wakehurst Place, the other principal arboretum belonging to the Royal Botanical Gardens, it is estimated that half the specimens were lost. Heart-breaking stories of historic trees blown down came from Scotney House in Kent, Blickling Hall in Norfolk, and Clandon House in Surrey. A sweet chestnut at Petworth, more than forty metres high and regarded as the tallest ever seen, failed to survive, and six of the historic seven oaks at Sevenoaks were lost. They lay untidily like giant broccoli stalks on the immaculate green. At least a thousand mature trees were lost in Hampton Court and Bushey Park – the park in which I walk my dogs. Hampstead Heath 'looked like seven jumbo jets had landed on it'. But it's an ill wind that blows no good. Rare trees were amongst those which suffered, and carpenters, cabinet-makers, and timber-merchants enjoyed themselves. They would have enjoyed themselves more if many well-meaning councils had not been quite so enthusiastic with their chain-saws.

Shanklin Pier, Portsmouth Cathedral, the minaret of the Brighton Royal Pavilion and the pinnacle of the tower of Chichester Cathedral, caravan parks and cross-channel ferries, a row of cottages near Canterbury, blocks of flats and glasshouses everywhere, a hotel in Windsor . . . it was an appalling catalogue of destruction.

There were bizarre incidents. Thirty-seven Tamils, detained on the Earl William ferry at Harwich, were allowed ashore when their floating prison broke from its moorings and was holed. Shingle, imported from Holland at a cost to the Government of £12 million, was washed away overnight. Looters were observed. A man was charged with stealing a clarinet from a damaged shop, and three men partly buried in the ruins of a block of flats in Lancing were dusted down and charged with breaking and entering.

Only eighteen people died, four of them from falling chimney stacks. Had the storm taken place during daylight hours the havoc doesn't bear thinking about.

The effect of the storm must have been greatest on the population's psyche. It is no small thing when, unheralded and unexplained, a force is released more stupendous than could be produced by all the H-bombs, the generating stations, and the stock piles of explosives simultaneously self-destructing. 'The wind bloweth where it listeth and thou hearest the sound thereof, but canst not tell whence it cometh, and whither it goeth'. Did people who had not prayed since childhood mutter a desperate prayer on the night of 15 and 16 October 1987? I know I did.

An official probe into the forecasting débâcle cleared Michael Fish and Bill Giles of any blame but criticized the staff of the Met Office for inflexibility and sticking too rigidly to computer predictions. One huge advantage of the new technology is that when things go seriously wrong one can always blame the computer. But there remains something desperately lame about the official excuse which, while putting the blame on the incompatibility of computer models in different countries, exonerated any individual from censure. It seems that we needed a scapegoat, and that the nation seized on Bill Giles and Michael Fish for that role. They remained unapologetic, and in time one came almost to believe that these two uncharismatic fellows had not only failed to forecast the hurricane, but had somehow been responsible for it.

Most of my childhood and adolescence was spent in and around the Quarry Woods which may be found between Henley and Maidenhead. These were the 'big bad woods' of Kenneth Grahame's imagination. They are fine mature beeches, with the occasional conifer and silver birch. There are piles of flints, which I was told had been 'broken up by prisoners of war', though to what purpose I couldn't imagine. There's a hollow lane, concealed by branches and shrubbery, which few people know about. To me this lane was Walter de la Mare's 'Road Through the Woods' and I imagined that he had based his poem upon it. One day, walking my dog through the woods, I noticed that many of the trees had been painted with numbers, and shortly afterwards these trees had been cut down. For days thereafter they lay on their sides, their sap bleeding out of them. Then numbers appeared on other of the trees. There were petitions, and explanations. 'The trees needed thinning', 'the losses would soon be made good', and so on. In time they were, but then came October 1987 and January and February 1990. The trouble with the Quarry Woods is that they grow out of the steep hillsides of the southernmost end of the Chilterns. The trees are tall and the roots are shallow. When I first visited the Quarry Woods early in 1990 I could not believe my eyes. Three quarters of the trees were down. What men with saws and axes had nibbled at, the storms had bitten off in vast mouthfuls. We need not have conducted our protests, signed and circulated our petitions.

There is a strong temptation to be sentimental about nature. But the regularity of the seasons is possibly the most important defence we have against fears of mortality. The first snowdrop in February, the first catkin, the first violet, is a reassurance that something of us too will survive death; no wonder we view violent alterations in the seasons with concern; no wonder extremes of weather cause national unease. We are disturbed to our very souls.

I thought of the Quarry Woods when I settled down to research and write this book. I hoped that I would find evidence that what we have been experiencing in the last few years, sizzling heat, unremitting drought, terrifying floods, and tumultuous storms, are nothing untoward. That what we have been experiencing in our national weather is similar to what we have always experienced. Talk of 'the greenhouse effect' and 'holes in the ozone layer' is no more than predictable gossip in an era in which every journalist is a scientist, and every scientist a scaremonger. I was reassured to find that, while many meteorologists insist that the climate is getting warmer, there are plenty to argue that, on the contrary, it is getting colder. I recalled those tedious attacks on the BBC. The Tory Party is convinced that the Corporation is irredeemably Left, while the Glasgow Media Group has powerful evidence that it remains, as it has always been, decidedly Right. Attacked for leaning too far in both directions, Auntie remains to her credit staunchly upright.

So I hoped I would find that the seasons are still sacrosanct, that Somerset is not about to sizzle up, nor Essex disappear under the North Sea. Let me tell you what I did find.

2

. . . .

Were There Tree Rings
in Eden?

'And God saw that it was good.'
Genesis

D id somebody called Noah really survive a flood? And if so,
when? And where? And does it matter?

To take the easy question first, it clearly matters to fundamentalists, who will in any case be unperturbed and un-
concerned about scientific and scholarly evidence. Those who
believe every word of the Bible are as unyielding and misguided
as those who believe every word of their daily horoscopes.
When we come to deal with the greenhouse effect, an unhelpful
but vivid piece of jargon, and the apocalypse option (ditto), it is
some comfort to know that a human race which has survived at
least one flood will probably survive another. It is perfectly
possible that a modern Noah would take his brood to Mars or the
moon, and, instead of sending back a dove, would send back a
communications satellite. So *was* there a flood?

There is a story similar to the story of Noah's Ark in the Epic of
Gilgamesh. Gilgamesh ruled early in the third millennium before
Christ, but the story predates Gilgamesh. It seems that the Gods
had grown tired of the endless racket made by humans and had
decided that there was to be a flood. They informed a fortunate
man called Utanapishtim suggesting that the sensible thing for
him to do was to tear down his house made of reeds, and build a
boat.

'The wind and flood raged for six days and nights, but on the
seventh day the stormy wind exhausted itself and died down

and the flood water receded. I surveyed the scene and the earth was silent. Man and all his works turned to mud and clay. I opened a hatch and daylight fell upon my face. I wept as I looked for signs of life. On the twelfth day I could see a dozen patches of land sticking out of the water. The ship eventually grounded on Mount Nisir, and it stayed there for six days until we got out.'

Utanapishtim survived to old age and passed on the tale to King Gilgamesh, through whom it was immortalized. It is quite possible that when Abraham, or somebody like him, left Sumeria for Canaan, he took the story of the Flood with him, which would explain how it became a part of the Genesis story. The excavations of Ur, a Sumerian city, in the Twenties, revealed a layer of silt consistent with a great flood about halfway through the third millennium.

It is possible that the Bible story is entirely independent of the Gilgamesh story. But that would only suggest that tales of a huge inundation from which only a few survived were common to more than one culture, and therefore likely to be based on a real event or events.

If we date the Gilgamesh flood to the early fourth or late third millennium before Christ, how should we date Noah's flood? Biblical and Rabbinical scholars work it out by backdating the genealogies, calculating an average for each generation. Archbishop Ussher came up with a date of 2349 BC for the flood, the Septuagint reckoned it at 2242 BC, and the Rabbis at 2103 BC. If the inconsistencies surprise you, try undertaking the mathematics yourself!

The Bible may be divinely inspired but it is mathematically suspect. Noah is said to have been five hundred years old when he received his instructions from God, and it took him a hundred years to construct his ark. Sir Walter Raleigh took leave to doubt (in *The Historie of the World*) whether the ark could possibly have been big enough to contain all the animals and birds, along with Noah's family and food and water for forty days and nights. (They would scarcely have worried about water though.) Attempts by geologists and archaeologists to find evidence of a great inundation have been disappointing. But there is no doubt that when the Israelites lived in Egypt, floods would have been common occurrences.

Archaeologists have hunted high, and more frequently low, for evidence of a great flood at about the time that there should have been one, if the Bible is to be believed. Tree rings, silt layers, peat bogs, beetles and pollen counts have yielded nothing to give credence to the fundamentalists. If there was a flood when there ought to have been a flood, it was an extremely secretive one.

On the other hand a study for the Royal Society and the National Environment Council prepared in 1989 by Professor Ian Gass insists that for the past one and a half million years the world's climate has been markedly unstable. There have been seventeen periods when the weather in the middle latitudes – and that includes us – has been significantly colder than it is today – probably by about nine degrees. But between 7,000 and 4,000 BC we were in the middle of the Holocene period and the world was warmer than it had been for 100,000 years, and warmer than it has ever been since. (It was warmer still during the Jurassic and Cretaceous Periods between 200 million and 60 million years ago.) Research into fossils of flora and fauna suggests that the changes from a temperate climate to polar extremes happened astonishingly rapidly, within decades or centuries, possibly even within years. There is no evidence that these fluctuations have stopped or will stop happening. Another professor, Michael Miller of Cincinnati, who has been investigating sediment samples from the Amazon Basin, reports that the Amazonians experienced a temperature drop of between six and nine degrees 25,000 years ago, and catastrophic flooding between 600 and AD 1000, too late for Noah.

There are other pertinent questions to be asked about the Bible stories, and the meteorologist Gary Lockhart has impertinently asked some of them:

'The events after the flood are even more suspicious. Where did the three million cubic metres of water go? How did Noah get the marsupials to Australia and New Zealand?' (Or any animals to America, come to that.) 'How did genetics allow Noah to have a black son, a yellow son, and a white son?'

Years ago, as a schoolboy, I myself asked how Adam and Eve could have given rise to so many variegated races, to be told that it was obvious, wasn't it? Clearly they must have been albinotic negroes. These are questions incapable of satisfactory answers, and the next pair of well-dressed fundamentalists who come calling at my house on Saturday mornings may get more than they bargained for!

An interesting place, Egypt, for the beginning of civilization as we know it. A country which has few extremes of weather, but which depends upon the benevolence of the Nile to irrigate but not overflow the land. Herodotus reports in his History (Book 2, Chapter 13) that 'when Moeris was king, the Nile overflowed all Egypt below Memphis, as soon as it rose so little as eight cubits'. Almost a thousand years later, according to Herodotus, 'unless the river rise sixteen, or, at the very least, fifteen cubits, it does not overflow the lands'. He concludes that there seems to be a very real danger that Egypt may become, like Greece, a country dependent upon rain from heaven rather than irrigation from a river, and therefore subject to the whims of God, who 'may some day see fit not to grant the Greeks rain, but shall afflict them with a long drought', in which case they may be 'swept away by a famine'.

Herodotus was only one of many Greek writers concerned with the weather. Aristotle's Meteorologica and On Weather Signs by his pupil, Theophrastus, were scientific investigations of the weather at a time when it was possible for an educated citizen to have a smattering of all the knowledge that was available in the world. The weather impinged on all the other sciences, notably agriculture and military strategy. Anticipating the likely direction of the wind proved a formidable advantage for the Athenians at the Battle of Salamis.

Herodotus might almost have been writing for today's tabloids when he deduced probable disasters from climatic changes. I find it consoling that all those centuries ago people were just as worried as we are about catastrophic changes in the weather. Yet the Egyptians who were dependent upon successful irrigation had less to worry about from the vagaries of the weather than the Hebrews who colonized an area very much dependent upon the climate. The latter chose well, a place bounded on three sides by desert, but with fertile valleys and cooling sea breezes. It is interesting to remember that just as they left the delta behind, so they left pantheism behind. They would need the weather to be kind, and they would need a single benevolent creator to ensure that, if they deserved it to be, it would be. The flood is in Genesis, which precedes Exodus, so – for the most part – it was.

It was God in a pillar of a cloud by day which led the Israelites 'to search out a resting place for them' (Numbers 10.33). And when the Israelites grew mutinous at the endless diet of manna, it was the wind of God which rained quails upon them (Numbers 11.31). What is the first blessing in Deborah and Barak's Song of Thanksgiving?

'The earth trembled, and the heavens dropped, the clouds also dropped water. The mountains melted from before the Lord, even that Sinai from before the Lord God of Israel' (Judges 5.4–5).

It may be thought that I am dwelling at too great a length on the weather in the Middle East such a very long time ago. After all this is a book primarily concerned with the weather in contemporary Britain. And yet in both the Old and New Testaments of the Bible, in Homer and in any book of myths and legends you care to choose, you will find that the influence of the weather is paramount. It is God or the Gods who send us the weather, who reward us or punish us with it. In times of drought we still pray for rain. And when men come to believe that they are gods, they pour oil into the sea, smoke into the sky, and plan worse cataclysms than we have dared to imagine.

The weather is unpredictable, the climate is not. What we have been doing to the climate is something which will be dealt with in a later chapter. Whether we can find a modern Moses to lead us out of the land of ecological disaster remains problematic – and do we still have the faith to believe in miracles?

3

. . . .

Mr Fothergill's Sweet Peas

'What men call gallantry, and Gods adultery
Is much more common where the climate's sultry.'
George Byron – *Don Juan*

There is even a word for it: Biometeorology, the study of the effects of the atmosphere on living things. Everything that lives or breathes or has its being responds to, or anticipates, changes in the weather. Only *homo sapiens* writes about it. High winds increase our output of adrenalin. Warm winds like the *sharay* in Israel, or the Swiss *Foehn*, increase the serotonin levels in the blood, and add to our stress, migraines, anxiety, colic, irritability and insomnia. Extremes of temperature are bad for us, especially bad for the old, subject to hypothermia in the cold and heart attacks in the heat. How ironic that our attempts to control the temperature through air conditioning should have led to the spread of Legionnaire's Disease through evaporative condensers. If extremes of cold and heat can alike prove fatal, and if air conditioning is itself a killer, we are entitled, I should think, to feel as much stress in anticipation of what the weather might do as if both the *sharay* and the *Foehn* were blowing simultaneously through our living room.

But of course where the weather is concerned the British are not badly off at all. The average July temperature in London is about 17.8°, much the same as most other cities on a similar latitude, warmer than Newfoundland, colder than Winnipeg. In January however the differences are acute. Nowhere as far north as London enjoys such balmy winters. In the Yablonoi Mountains of Eastern Siberia the average is −37°. That is exceptional, but Berlin, Omsk and Kiev shiver while in London a January average of 4.4° is pleasantly bracing. In the savage February of 1991, the newspapers were cock-a-hoop over the discovery that Bournemouth was colder than Moscow. It is an indication of just how pampered we are that the item should have been considered newsworthy.

Yes, we are pampered; and our obsession with the extremes of our temperate climate arise from our refusal to accept that our climate could ever be anything but temperate. If it is uneconomic to keep a fleet of gritting lorries permanently serviced for the rare occasions when heavy snowfalls or severe frosts require their use, we can scarcely complain – though we do, and how we do! – when our transport system lets us down.

The present-day climate of the British Isles is both a good deal warmer than it used to be and a good deal colder. This paradox, which is not really a paradox at all, stems from whether you choose to begin your measurements in the Ice Age some 20,000 years ago or what is rather grandly called the Interglacial Maximum some 8,000 years ago. The evidence suggests that 20,000 years ago the mean temperature in Britain was about 10° colder, while 8,000 ago it was 2° warmer than it is today. The seventeenth century coincided with the extremes of the Little Ice Age, keeping the temperature an average degree or two colder. Thereafter the evidence of primitive thermometers, and the proliferation of diarists, give us substantial and detailed information for the first time of what was happening to our weather.

The summers of 1665 and 1666 were hot ones, 1666 being especially hot in London during the Great Fire. But the winter of 1683–4 was a wicked one. John Evelyn, the great diarist records:

'Men and cattle perishing in divers places, and the very seas locked up with ice that no vessels could stir out or come in. The fowls, fish and birds, and all our exotic plants and greens universally perishing. Many packs of deer destroyed, and all sorts of fuel so dear that there were contributions to keep the poor alive . . . London, by reason of the excessive coldness of the air hindering the ascent of the smoke, was so filled with this fuliginous steam of sea-coal that hardly could one see across the streets; and this filling the lungs with its gross particles exceedingly obstructed the breath, so as no one could scarcely breathe. There was no water to be had from the pipes and engines; nor could the brewers and other divers tradesmen work; and every moment was full of disastrous accidents . . .'

Since 1684 we know that in London the Thames froze sufficiently on a further seven occasions for frost fairs to be held on the ice.

Our benevolent weather results directly from the North Atlantic Drift, also known misleadingly as the Gulf Stream (it is not a lot to do with a Gulf and is not at all like a Stream). The Gulf Stream flows north-east from the Gulf of Mexico, becomes diverted by the appendix shape of Florida dangling into the Atlantic, then surges along the Atlantic sea-board of North America. Somewhere off Newfoundland it suffers an identity crisis and turns into the North Atlantic Drift. The drift, a warm current amidst cooler Atlantic waters, laps gently against Portugal and Brittany, floods genially onto the beaches of Cornwall, Ireland and Western Scotland and carries its influence further north to Iceland, Norway, and the mysterious island of Novaya Zemlya.

Off the coast of Cornwall the variation in the temperature of the sea between winter and summer is six degrees Centigrade. Plunge into the sea off the rocks at Kynance Cove and the cold will shock you rigid. No wonder you shiver as on a warm summer's afternoon you plunge into the sea at Kynance Cove, but dive in on a wicked December morning and you will be pleasantly surprised. The coldest place for a winter plunge is not Cornwall, nor the north of Scotland, nor the west of Ireland, all of which enjoy the benefit of the Drift, but the Norfolk coast. Prevailing Atlantic winds carry the warm air over the Drift to most of Britain, and even when easterly and north-easterly winds predominate, the sea around our coasts acts as a comforting muffler.

During a bitter snap in January and February 1956,

temperatures at Heathrow were about nine degrees less severe than at De Bilt Airport in the Netherlands. During the warmest summer for many years, the thermometer stopped short of 38. Few of us appreciate how well off we are.

Nor do we know how to respond when faced with extremes of temperature. Consider this true story from the long hot summer drought of 1989.

In the garden of Upper Morin Road, Paignton, Miss Kathleen Baker, JP, tended her sweet peas in the house she had lived in for sixty years. They were the packet variety known as 'Mr Fothergill's Mixed Sweet Peas' which are scheduled to flower between June and October. The Paignton Flower Club show took place on 24 June, but the prolonged dry weather meant that the sweet peas were not to be in full flower until July. Miss Baker was probably not too concerned with the flower show so long as they made the riot of colour in her garden which Mr Fothergill's packet promised.

Almost as if it were deliberately trying to make the Paignton Flower Show a success, South West Water delayed imposing a hosepipe ban until 25 June. The flower show came and went, but there was another horticultural treat in store.

Next to Miss Baker lived Mr John Webb, a mature student and at the time a hotel gardener, making sure that everything was neat and colourful for the Torbay In Bloom competition. Mr John Webb very much wanted to buy Miss Baker's house, but she was not about to sell. 'I had no intention of leaving and told him I didn't think he would like my price,' she said.

Mr Webb responded by announcing that he was considering knocking a hole between the Webb flat and the Baker loft, so that Mr Webb Junior could get a proper run for his model trains.

In irritation, desperation and pique, Mr Webb photographed Miss Baker watering her garden in defiance of the ban and sent it to the authorities. Miss Baker, in the court on whose bench she had sat with such dignity for so many years, admitted using a hosepipe during the ban but claimed in her defence that the water came from a recycled rainwater tank she had installed.

'Anyway,' she said, 'the photograph must have been taken in May because the blooms on Mr Fothergill's sweet peas are so small.' She directed the court's attention to the photograph. It studied it. Although the photograph was extremely fuzzy, the court supported Miss Baker, though why Mr Webb should have wanted a photograph of Miss Baker watering her garden in May in a perfectly legal manner remains a mystery.

Cleared of all charges Miss Baker received £250 costs from central funds and Mr Webb was quoted as saying: 'I am not happy about it. It is making me look a fool.'

The same year a devoted gardener from Brixham was successfully fined by South West Water after having been reported on three occasions by his neighbours. The seventy-year-old remained defiant, and vowed, 'I'd do it again. I've paid for the water and I'm entitled to use it. It's not my fault if they haven't got it. I've got a lovely garden which I've spent hundreds of pounds on and if it was dying I'd do the same thing again . . . This fine is a cheap way of saving my garden.'

Hosepipe bans were reimposed throughout much of the country the following summer, and once again it was Devonians who made the news. A Mr Stuart Hughes of Sidmouth attached his hosepipe to a watering can into which he had inserted a ballcock mechanism. Consequently the flow of water to his beloved plants was discontinuous and did not, in Mr Hughes's view, break the law. Thames Water had already ruled that a hosepipe in a watering can qualified as a sprinkler and was therefore illegal when a ban was in force, but had said nothing about ballcocks. An interesting, not to say suggestive, question which was never tested in the courts was, 'Does the ban still count if somebody else holds my hosepipe?'

In their attempts to come to terms with the weather the captains and kings of industry face complicated problems.

The scene is an engineering company in the north of England. The temperature is nudging the nineties and likely to remain so. The Deputy Chief Accountant arrives for work in shorts and sandals. The Chief Accountant is distinctly unhappy, and discusses the situation with the Director of Personnel. The Director of Personnel's advice is to send him home. 'He is asking for a confrontation and you cannot back off without losing your grip on discipline.'

The Chief Accountant sends his Deputy home to change. Within an hour the shop-floor is buzzing with the rumour that a director has been sacked for wearing a T-shirt to a board meeting. One can appreciate the view that shorts and sandals may not inspire confidence in those upon whose goodwill a large export order may depend. But neither do pools of damp under the arms. The Director General of the Institute of Personnel Management reported that during the heatwave he carried his jacket folded in his briefcase for the journey to work, because, even if he never put it on, he felt naked without it. A letter to *The Times* answered the question of how to keep organized and cool. Ian Millar suggested that since wallet, credit cards, cheque-book, diary, pen, key ring, spectacles, pocket comb and folding scissors clearly would not fit into trouser pockets a sleeveless fisherman's jacket could be worn, 'light and cool with nine pockets or so of assorted size. I am not a fisherman myself, and I find the long pocket at the back meant for a fish will hold a folded copy of *The Times*.'

We are in any case a nation of uniform wearers. Those whose importance lies in inspiring the rest of us with their dependability, their incorruptibility, and their ineffable wisdom – I refer, you will have gathered, to top members of the professions, such as lawyers, judges, policemen, doctors, scientists, and bishops, though not, perhaps surprisingly, Members of Parliament – wear uniforms. And those who aspire to become top members of their chosen professions do the best they can with brogues and pin-stripe.

However, there are signs that after a series of hot summers the formalities may be easing. Male bank clerks are no longer required to wear suits when serving customers, although ties remain obligatory. Women enjoy greater latitude, in part because an employer appears so foolish in trying to impose

21

regulations. A skirt six inches above the knee may seem almost modest on a gazelle-like clerk, almost obscene on a dumpy one. The American influence on the British businessman was significant in the Seventies – Apple Computers was just one of several transatlantic companies that stressed informality – but the Japanese, impeccably clad in lightweight three-piece suits, and often carrying rolled-up umbrellas, bucked the trend.

There have been other developments which have encouraged the metropolitan businessman or businesswoman to change their lifestyle. One is air-conditioning, another is sandwich bars with take-out services.

Air-conditioning is pleasant enough, but poses sartorial problems. How do you dress for the sizzling streets without shivering at work? The sandwich bars provide one solution. Why venture out into the blazing heat at all when it is perfectly possible to stay in the office and remain cool and in control? The idea of a crowded and sweltering pub as you queue at the food counter for steak and kidney pudding is an unappealing alternative.

It may well be that, if we continue to enjoy hot summers, we shall come to adopt the Australian habit of starting and finishing work early, with plenty of opportunity to relax in the cool of the afternoon sun. Or the continental siesta. Or the policy of Romans and Parisians who abandon their cities during the heat of the summer, when no mortal can be expected to achieve much anyway, returning relieved and refreshed for the autumn. In Rome skeleton staffs man a few offices while the local council arranges that enough cafés and bars remain open to feed and water those who staunchly remain. Increasingly sophisticated technology means that more and more executives will soon be able to conduct a good deal of their work from an air-conditioned home or by the side of their pool.

4

Spiders' Webs and Supercomputers

'I always avoid prophesying beforehand, because it is a much better policy to prophesy after the event has taken place.'

Sir Winston Churchill (1943)

❋

'It's quite flattering that people complain when we get the weather forecast wrong. Several years ago they did not expect it to be right.'

Suzanne Charlton, forecaster and presenter on BBC Television

'When it is evening, ye say, it will be fair weather, for the sky is red. And in the morning, it will be foul weather today, for the sky is red and lowering' (Matthew 16.2–3).

If the author of the gospel of St Matthew and the anonymous author of the well-known couplet: 'Red sky at night, shepherd's delight, Red sky in the morning, shepherd's warning,' are in agreement as to the basics of weather forecasting, who needs experts? Who, to be precise, needs one of the world's most powerful computers, the Cray YMP Supercomputer running a fluid dynamics atmospheric model at the Meteorological Office in Bracknell, which can handle 800 million operations a second, and probably tell you the time if you ask it politely? The battle between amateur countryman and meteorological technician is a continuing one, and as many swear by their little bit of seaweed as by the anodyne tones of the broadcasting expert.

It was not only the disasters of October 1987 which gnawed away at the authority of the experts. Long before, a process had begun to make household pets out of the weather men, so that

Bill Giles, or Michael Fish, or Ian McCaskill, found themselves feted and empanelled. It was their innocence that made them seem so appealing. In a world of Grecian 2000 and Armani outfits, these were men with metaphorical mud on their boots. Not for them the authoritative white coats of the advertiser's technicians, pouring mysterious fluids from test-tube to pipette while expatiating in honeyed tones on the remarkable properties of this cough mixture, or that panacea for dandruff. The livery for a weatherman was the cardigan, and occasionally the polyester-mix sports jacket.

Any woman who dared to venture into the world of isobars and remotely controlled meteorological maps was severely coiffured and garbed in whatever seemed five years out of date. One sympathized with these women but one felt even sorrier for them when they too were given the treatment, turning up with brazenly open necks to open supermarkets. The irony is that these men and women, Bill, Suzanne and Michael, John, Ian and Frances, Sian and Alex, are all trained meteorologists. Trish Williamson and Ulrika Jonsson, however, who rose from the ranks of 'breakfast television', are not.

The attempt to create authoritative figures whose erratic charts and anxious eyes would persuade the nation that 'They Knew Best' was backfiring, because how could one believe the word of a personality who agreed to appear on an inane quiz show? Can one imagine that the uncompromising and funereal Jack Scott, not the first BBC weatherman, but the most austere, would ever agree to participate in such shenanigans?

Britain's most famous and beloved weather sage is Bill Foggitt – a man with a perfect name which has undoubtedly contributed to his success. But even Foggitt nods. Here is *The Times* for 11 March 1988:

'Bill Foggitt, the seventy-five-year-old weather sage from Thirsk, North Yorkshire, is waiting intently for nature's signposts to confirm his belief that we are in for a long hot summer.

'Yesterday he saw two magpies looking for a nesting site – a sure sign that spring is just around the corner. Now he is watching out for the first frog spawn, generally a reliable indicator.

'It nearly always arrives in his pond around 26–27 March. If it is in the middle of the pond it usually means a dry summer because the frogs don't want to risk laying where the perimeter might dry out . . .'

There is more in the same folksy vein, but the May that followed was one of the wettest on record; Barnsley and Wakefield were underwater in June, and the rest of the summer continued drenchingly wet, especially in North Yorkshire.

There the story might have rested, except that on 13 April 1990, just two years and a month later than the previous report we read the following in *The Times*:

'Noting the early appearance of frogspawn in his garden pond, rooks building nests high in the trees and spiders spinning long strands to their webs, Mr Bill Foggitt, the celebrated amateur weather forecaster, yesterday predicted a "pretty good" summer.'

Mr Foggitt, who may be bought a pint in the Three Tuns, Thirsk, is certainly good value. He speaks of a friend of his mother's: 'Whenever she declined to have jam on her toast at tea we knew there was thunder on the way.'

You will be no more surprised than I was to learn from the *Financial Times* (19 December 1989) that Mr Foggitt's talents are in increasing demand, nor that he has gone into product endorsement with an optician marketing a range of weather symbol spectacles (whatever they may be). I am only surprised that he has not yet marketed frogspawn.

There are serious rivals to Bill.

Arthur Mackins of Chichester is five years senior at eighty-three, and depends less on frogspawn than on sunspots, responsible for a 'seven-year hot summer cycle', and spiders – 'If they build long frames to their webs, you can expect fine weather.' Now where else did I read that? As a retired bank clerk, Arthur has a head for figures, and has produced an interesting theory: 'It is a fact that since the war all the summers ending in nine – '49, '59, '69, '79, '89 – have been good, whereas all the eights have been disastrous.'

Frank Murray is a bee-keeper and allows his bees to do his forecasting for him. 'Their laying and hatching patterns are natural. The Queen can sense in advance when the weather will be hot.' The Met Office is dismissive of such claims, insisting that bees react to changes, rather than predicting them.

Chris Choy, a producer with Radio York, was unfortunate enough to be knocked to the ground by riot police in Gdansk. Ever since he has suffered from arthritis. But there is a bright side. When he feels a twinge he knows that there will be rain within six or seven hours. Comments Mr Clifford Smith, weatherman:

'There are [sic] a minority of people who are susceptible to rapid pressure changes and may feel them in their bones. The trouble is they are likely to react in the same way whether the pressure is rising or falling.'

Piers Corbyn, who lectures in maths at the South Bank Polytechnic in London, uses a computer to analyse the data he receives from the Met Office, adding his own personal touch by taking sunspot activity into account. Then he places bets with William Hills and, if you believe what you read in the newspapers, wins substantially and regularly. What must satisfy him as much as the pocket money is that William Hills sets the odds on advice from the Met Office. With the help of colleagues and some of his winnings Piers has set up a company, Weatherplan Services, to market his predictions. It has had some success. Companies are desperate for accurate weather information and cannot afford to lose out to rivals who receive better information. It is not so much that Weatherplan's results have been scintillatingly successful as that they could become so. More than forty companies pay an annual subscription of £1,000 each for the monthly bulletins; the company has many private customers too. Weatherplan ran into stormy waters in the summer of 1991. The company anticipated a warm, sunny June.

It was the coldest June on record. The forecast of 'a rain-free Wimbledon' was speedily followed by torrential downpours forcing the abandonment of much of the first week's play.

Corbyn explained these embarrassing incidents upon unexpected sunspot activity, and correctly forecast a fine July. 'Sunspots? That's astronomy not meteorology,' snorted Michael Fish. Philip Eden, the guru of high technology forecasting, was publicly derisory:

'If his July forecast is wrong,' he is quoted as saying, 'he will no doubt find some other excuse such as the volcanic eruption in the Philippines. I'm surprised he didn't use that for June, but maybe he's saving it up.'

The youngish and personable Philip Eden markets his forecasts to newspapers and commercial radio stations. His equipment is an Acorn Archimedes, with additional hard disc and high resolution display – software from Spacetech of Dorset. The Archimedes takes pictures from Meteosat 4, a satellite which sits above the equator at 0 degrees latitude and 0 degrees longitude, with cameras sensitive to the infra red end of the spectrum. The comparative temperatures over the last eight hours of land, sea and cloud show up in shades and colours on the Archimedes screen. Meteosat sends pictures every half hour, and these pictures can be linked to produce pretty and informative animations. They are the pictures you can see daily on your television screens. Together with Radiofax from Germany, the American WIS Database – American Express has marketed a forecasting telephone service in the US for seventy five cents a minute and you can even find out what the weather is likely to be on the moon – and a Dell 210 computer at the London Broadcasting Company in Hammersmith, Philip Eden offers a service which the country clearly appreciates. 'I am very against waving your arms around in front of the same old graphics every day,' he says.

Are his predictions more accurate than the Met Office forecasts issued by the BBC and those newspapers Eden does not write for? (The Met Office also takes the Meteosat pictures.)

What matters most is that people appear to think they are. You get what you pay for, and what you wish to believe. (It is delightfully ironic that immediately after the BBC started to pay the Weather Office for its forecasts in 1989 Britain enjoyed one of its finest summers for many years.)

Philip Eden's Archimedes information is accurate for Britain because the satellite is positioned directly on the Greenwich meridian, but for international forecasts – and that means longer-range forecasts – one needs a polar orbiting satellite some 500 miles up in space. This useful little creature will transmit pictures of a different strip of the earth's surface with each orbit as the planet rotates through 25 per cent of longitude. For a more complete list of the various weather satellites and communication systems, see Appendix III.

Such is the present interest in weather forecasting, and the importance for many people of knowing what the weather is likely to do, that British Aerospace and an American company, Dartcom, have produced a satellite receiving dish and desk-top computer system, retailing for less than £5,000, to enable those who are IBM compatible to produce their own forecasts. They will offer serious competition to such companies as International Weather Predictions, which has several industrial customers for its predictions including the Civil Aviation Authority, which pays them £18 million a year.

The Met Office has been able to move into marketing as a result of being granted 'executive agency status' from the Ministry of Defence. While still state-owned the Office is allowed to spend part of its budget in the private sector, and anything it makes in profits may be ploughed back into research. So it is the Met Office which negotiated a contract with Power Gen to supply weather forecasts to ITN. It also runs Site Wise for the construction industry and Open Road for local authorities, who may spend £10,000 in a single night salting and gritting the roads, only to find that the temperature stays infuriatingly above freezing. Then there are travel agents, British Rail and oil companies prepared at critical moments to take a weather expert on board a rig at a cost of £300 a day. Bakers, ice-cream companies, and Sophie Mirman's ill-fated Sock Shops have all thought it worthwhile to employ the Met Office and have been willing to cough up for accurately targeted information.

British Gas has estimated that for each centigrade degree the temperature rises 4 per cent is lopped from the demand for gas. But the bitter January of 1987 produced increased net profits of £100 million. The glorious summer of 1989 increased beer sales in the UK by between 5 per cent and 10 per cent, but what brewers really enjoy is sultry, muggy weather. Dry heat, it seems, chiefly benefits the manufacturers of soft drinks. Drinks and ice cream sales improve as soon as the weather does. But it takes two consecutive fine days for people to start cycling to work, and a week of sunshine before people buy sun tan lotion. These are heady times for those who can accurately predict the weather.

But the problem with forecasting the weather is that the technology only offers useful advantages in the short term. The best analogy is with a chess game. There is little difficulty in programming a chess computer with all the information contained in *Modern Chess Openings*, the chess-players' Bible. This will give the computer the latest information on how to achieve a strong position after a dozen or so moves. But thereafter the slightest variation proliferates alarmingly, leading within a few more moves to an almost infinite number of positions, more than even the largest computer can analyse. In this middle-game the experienced chessplayer has the advantage of his or her instincts, which rule out a whole range of moves, and can concentrate on what appears to be the 'strongest' one. Often the player cannot adequately explain why this move is strong. It just *feels* strong.

So meteorologists enjoy a party game which involves starting up two almost identical weather programmes on their computers and watching the projections diverge. They do dramatically. The delightful saying that the flap of a butterfly's wings in a garden may in time affect the route of a tropical storm was first used in 1979 in a lecture on the Chaos Theory in Climatology to the American Association for the Advancement of Science and referred to a butterfly in Brazil and a tornado in Texas. It has since been much distorted. It is as scientifically authentic as to suppose that, if you had recording equipment of sufficient sensitivity, you would be able to hear Shakespeare and Anne Hathaway courting in Anne's garden, or Jesus delivering the Sermon on the Mount.

Despite the delivery to the Met Office of their giant new Cray YMP 832 Computer, it will be years, perhaps decades, even centuries, before inaccurate weather forecasts become a part of history. The problem in the recent past is that when there are mistakes they are so public and can be so disastrous. The east coast floods of 1953, in which more than 300 people were drowned, and the great storm of 1987 are tragic examples. But the storms of January and February 1990 were accurately anticipated. On 26 February the highest tides ever recorded in the City of Liverpool were correctly forecast, as well as the Towyn floods which had such appalling effects on the community.

Britain's weather is principally affected by what takes place in the Atlantic Ocean. More than a hundred depressions a year sweep in and most of these are more than 1,000 kilometres wide. The depressions have their origins in minute variations in climatic conditions in the tropics, and there are very few observers, human or mechanical, in the empty vastnesses of the tropical Pacific.

There was a time when weather ships doubled as beacons for international airlines. Consequently it was profitable to keep them sailing. Now they are extravagant indulgences and only a few remain on the high seas, one Russian, one French, two European, and the Cumulus.

The Cumulus has a crew of twenty, all volunteers. They send weather balloons aloft (as do a number of merchant ships), and sink probes deep into the ocean, sending hourly reports back to the Central Forecasting Office at Bracknell. The crew are inveterate bird-watchers and are regularly able to rescue exhausted land birds, hawks and owls that have been blown off course, and the occasional distressed sea-bird. Once the Cumulus picked up two Swedish airmen who had crashed into the sea.

Floating weather buoys go some way to remedy the lack of a fleet of weather ships but there is a limit to the amount of information these little creatures can absorb and relay.

The Central Forecasting Office also receives information from Snoopy, a Hercules transport plane flying out of Farnborough. It was Snoopy which was sent off to investigate the disintegrating ozone layers above the Arctic. Also, of course, from the weather satellites; but these are severely limited by cloud and are unable to measure wind speeds when there is cloud cover. The Meteosats cannot measure wind speeds at all north of the 45° latitude. The sea, the sky, and the atmosphere, yet still the forecasts are inadequate. What more can the meteorologists do?

A hugely ambitious programme is currently under way at the Deacon Laboratory in Wormley, Surrey. Here they are building electronic dolphins. I should say DOLPHINS. Deep Ocean Long Path Hydrographic Instruments – and I certainly hope there was a bonus for the boffin who thought up that acronym! These are – or will be – battery-powered robotic submarines no more than six metres long which can traverse the Atlantic at a depth of 7,000 metres. From time to time they will poke their noses up above the surface of the water to check their position from a passing GPS Navstar Satellite and send off data to a Meteosat.

Nor is that the limit of the Institute's ambitions. To scratch around the ocean bed with sophisticated sonar equipment it has designed a DOGGIE – Deep Ocean Geological and Geophysical Instrumented Explorer – which will even be able to explore regions never before tested by men or instruments, the sea-bed, for example, under the polar ice-caps.

Despite the technology, the vulgar sums of money invested, the scholarly research, the international cooperation, and the debates in parliament, the question still remains to be asked:

31

are weather forecasts any use? In 1987 a cynical group of students at Sheffield Polytechnic decided to test their theory – about which many of us have speculated – that forecasters would produce more accurate results if they were content to announce that tomorrow's weather would be just the same as today's. Their target was to predict whether or not it would rain in Sheffield tomorrow, which is surely the most urgent and basic question for most of those who tune in to the radio or television forecasts. And they set their results against those of the Leeds Weather Centre and the Met Office forecasts.

The Sheffield Weather Centre correctly forecast rain 67 per cent of the time. The Polytechnic students got it right 65.7 per cent of the time. The Met Office was correct 65.4 per cent of the time. Max Moulin, head of the Applied Statistics and Operational Research Department who had suggested the survey, commented: 'If all you want to know is whether or not to take an umbrella to work tomorrow or to arrange a picnic or barbecue, you will do as well looking out of the window today. You will get a pretty good idea of what the weather will be like.'

Nonetheless the newspapers continue to publish and the television screens to feature the ominous weather maps. And if you set more store by them than the Sheffield students, here are some hints as to how to interpret them.

The first thing to look for are the areas of low and high pressure. These are usually and helpfully marked 'Low' and 'High', but in any case low pressure systems can be identified by a thumbprint pattern of isobars. The closer these are together the more powerful the winds around the centre are likely to be; such a system is called a cyclone, and if violent enough it can grow into what is generally understood to be a cyclone. Winds blow anticlockwise in these cyclonic systems. High pressure areas are identified by spaces of nothing very much on the weather map. This is because the isobars are far apart, and there is very little that can be usefully shown on the chart.

Next you should identify the fronts, the areas of battle between opposing weather systems. Warm fronts are depicted with round bobbles, cold fronts with pointed spikes and occluded fronts, in which cold fronts are overtaking warm fronts, with alternating bobbles and spikes. Fronts move in the direction in which they point, and tend to travel in an expanding arc around a low. A typical weather map of Britain will show a series of lows with attached warm fronts moving eastwards from the Atlantic, and a series of highs over Scandinavia and Europe. Since these two frontal systems are often in opposition, we usually enjoy a constantly changing pattern of weather. Fine and settled periods of weather, cold in winter and warm in summer, result from a powerful high pressure system establishing itself over the British Isles; showery weather is caused when there is little opposition to the Atlantic depressions sweeping in up the Channel. It follows that when the prevailing winds are from the south and west the weather will be warmer; from the north and east cooler. Winds blowing clockwise around a high pressure system will tend to give cold frosty weather in winter, especially down the east coast. Warm and wet turbulence will result from anticlockwise cyclonic patterns, and the barometer will fall sharply. A warm front from the continent meeting colder air over Britain can give rise to thundery conditions.

But if you are more of the Foggitt persuasion let me end this chapter with some of the old-fashioned rules for forecasting the weather.

The definitive anthology of weather lore is called simply: *Weather-lore*, compiled by R. Inwards and published by Elliot Stock in London in 1898. *The Shepherd of Banbury's Rules*, published by Mr Claridge in 1744, are too long to quote here, but consist of a typical amalgam of weather lore, based, it is claimed, on forty years of weather-watching. They probably owe something to the Greek astronomer, Theophrastus, and his Book of Signs, which gave no fewer than eighty different indications of rain. A selective use of the proverbs listed below, all of which relate to the UK, should enable you to become a regular sage on a local radio station at the very least, and might even be your secret to fame, fortune and over-exposure.

General Rules

Be it dry or be it wet
The weather'll always pay its debt.

Evening red and morning grey,
Two good signs for one fine day.
Evening grey and morning red,
Send the shepherd wet to bed.

When the wind is in the east,
'Tis neither good for man nor beast.
When the wind is in the West
Then the wind is at its best.

When the bees crowd out of their hive,
The weather makes it good to be alive.
When the bees crowd into the hive again,
It is a sign of thunder and of rain.

Pale moon does rain,
Red moon does blow,
White moon does neither rain nor snow.

Autumn months: Wheezy, Sneezy, Freezy.
Winter months: Slippy, Drippy, Nippy.
Spring months: Showery, Flowery, Bowery.
Summer months: Hoppy, Croppy, Poppy. (From
  Sheridan's Rhyming Calendar).

Optimistic Signs

Dew in the night
Next day will be bright.

When spiders' webs in air do fly,
The spell will soon be very dry.

Rain before seven
Fine before eleven.

(Or is the preceding old saw merely due to the requirements of the rhyme?)

> If woolly fleeces strew the heavenly way,
> Be sure no rain disturbs the summer day.
> When mulberry leaves are green,
> Then no more frosts are seen.

Rain

Oak before ash
Have a splash
Ash before oak
Have a soak.

A round-topped cloud with flattened base,
Carries rainfall in its face.

When eager bites the thirsty flea,
Clouds and rain you sure shall see.

If the clouds be bright, 'twill clear tonight,
If the clouds be dark, 'twill rain, will you hark.

When a cow tries to scratch its ear,
It means a shower is very near.
When it clumps its side with its tail,
Look out for thunder, lightning and hail.

If the cock goes crowing to bed
He'll certainly rise with a watery head.
If a fly lands on your nose, swat till it goes,
If the fly then lands again, it will bring back heavy rain.

When clouds appear like rocks and towers,
The earth will be refreshed by frequent showers.

When the stars begin to huddle
The earth will soon become a puddle.

When Bredon Hill puts on his hat,
Ye men of the Vale beware of that.

The bonnie moon is on her back;
Mend your shoes and sort your thack.

(The above is from Scotland, and seems directly contradicted
by the Welsh equivalent: 'It is sure to be a dry moon if it lies on its
back, so that you can hang your hat on its horns.')

Wind

Mackerel sky and mares' tails
Make tall ships carry low sails.

When clouds look as if scratched by a hen,
Get ready to reef your topsails then.

Long foretold, long last;
Short notice, soon past.

When the wind backs against the sun
Trust it not, for back it will run.
First rise after low
Foretells a stronger blow.

Frost

Many hips and haws,
Many frosts and snaws.

Through the Year

January

If the grass grows in January
It grows the worse for all the year.

A January spring is worth nothing

If the birds begin to sing in January,
Frosts are on the way.

13 January (St Hilary) is considered to be the coldest day of the year.

If St Paul's Day (25 January) be fair and clear,
Then it betides a happy year.

February

February fill dyke.

If Candlemas (2 February) be fair and bright,
Winter'll have another flight.
But if Candlemas be clouds and rain,
Winter is gone and will not come again.

A dry Lent means a fertile year.

February makes a bridge (referring to ice)
March breaks it.

March

March comes in like a lion,
Goes out like a lamb.

March dust on apple leaf
Brings all kind of fruit to grief.

Better to be bitten by a snake
Than to feel the sun in March.

March comes in with adders' heads,
And goes out with peacocks' tails.

As many misties in March
So many frosties in May.

March water and May sun
Make clothes clean and maidens dun.

As many mists in March as there are frosts in May.

Thunder in March, floods in May.

March winds and April showers
Bring forth May flowers.

(And yet April is one of the driest – as well as the cruellest –
months.)

April

Easter in snow, Christmas in mud,
Christmas in snow, Easter in mud.

If it rains on Easter Day,
There shall be good grass but very bad hay.

(But 'A wet May brings a good load of hay.')

April snows stay no longer than water on a trout's back.

April moist and warm makes farmers sing like nightingales.

A cold April and a full barn.

When April blows his horn (thunder),
'Tis good for hay and corn.

Cuckoo oats and woodcock hay
Makes a farmer run away.

May

A hot May makes a fat churchyard.

A cold May and a windy
Makes a fat barn and a findy (good weight).

A dry May and a dripping June
Brings everything in tune.

If you would your doctor pay
Leave your flannels off in May.

The maid who would be fair to view,
Let her lave her face in the early dew
On May Day in the morning.

The more murder in May,
The less in August and September.

June

Calm weather in June
Sets the corn in tune.

Or:

A leak in June
Sets the corn in tune.

If it rains on 8 June it foretells a wet harvest.

If St Vitus' Day (15 June) be rainy weather,
It will rain for thirty days together.

When it is hottest in June,
The corresponding days of next February will be coldest.

Before St John's Day (24 June) we pray for rain:
After that we get it anyhow.

If it rains on 27 June,
It will rain for seven weeks.

July

If it rains on St Mary's Day (2 July) it will rain for a month.

> Oh St Swithin (15 July) if thou'll be fair,
> For forty days shall rain nae mair,
> But if St Swithin's thou be wet,
> For forty days it raineth yet.

(St Swithin wished to be buried where the rain would fall on him. When attempts were made to move his body within Winchester Cathedral his spirit caused it to rain for forty days thereafter. Similar critical days on the continent are St Medard (8 June) in France, St Godelieve (27 July) in Belgium, and Seven Sleepers (27 June) in Germany. Statistics utterly disprove the old superstition regarding St Swithin's Day, and I suspect they would do the same for St Medard, St Godelieve, and the Seven Sleepers).

August

> If St Bartholomew's Day (24 August) be fair and clear,
> Then a prosperous autumn comes that year.

(No rhymes for August, so a sparse month for weather-lore!)

September

> If it does not rain on St Michael (29 September) and Gallus (16 October),
> The following spring will be dry and propitious.

October

St Luke's Little Summer refers to St Luke's Day (18 October) around which time there is often a period of fine, warm weather.

St Simon and St Jude (28 October) traditionally marks the end of this gentle time.

November

>Ice in November to bear a duck,
>The rest of the winter'll be slush and muck.

St Martin's Day (11 November) also is supposed to have its Little Summer.

December

>A green Christmas means a fat churchyard.

>Sun through the apple trees on Christmas Day,
>Means a fine crop is on the way.

5

Great Balls of Fire

'From lightening and tempest,
from Plague Pestilence and Famine,
from Battell and murder,
and from suddaine death,
Good Lord deliver us.'

Old Litany

Lightning shows a healthy disregard for caste or class. It was over a hundred in the shade – if you could find any – in Tamiami Park, Miami, in September 1987 when 300,000 of the faithful arrived to worship at an outdoor Mass given by the Pontiff. The bullet-proof Popemobile made two circuits of the ground, accompanied by eight cardinals, 30 bishops, a choir of 1,000 and a forty-six-piece orchestra. But just as the Pope was giving a well-prepared sermon condemning crime, corruption and contraception, in English, Haitian Creole and Spanish, lightning struck the ground directly in front of him. 'He jumped,' said witnesses, 'but quickly regained his composure and carried on.'

One cannot help being reminded of the unfortunate case of the Bishop of Durham, Dr David Jenkins, a controversialist, whose attacks on conventional Christianity had raised hackles in vicarage parlours throughout the land. Just a few days after his consecration in York Minster, lightning struck the spire of Europe's largest Gothic cathedral, and started a fire in the roof of the south transept, which was hideously damaged. The Rev. John Mowll of Buglawton, Cheshire, who had angrily intervened in the consecration service, announced that he did not rule out 'the possibility of divine intervention'. It was as though

Elijah had called forth the fire of the Lord upon the false prophets of Baal. Dr Runcie, then Archbishop of Canterbury, expected to give a lead in these matters, pooh-poohed the idea: 'When somebody claims for their position a divine intervention I am always very cautious, and think that people should be very cautious about such claims.' He is quoted as adding: 'It seems absolutely miraculous that the fire was confined to the Transept . . . The Lord was on our side as we battled with the flames.' Theologically this seems to put the Archbishop and the Lord in a dubious conspiracy, in no way responsible for the lightning, but very much involved in limiting the extent of the fire and repairing the damage caused by it.

One might expect Popes and Bishops to be obvious targets when they go off target themselves, and one of the barmier statistics provided in recent years seemed to suggest that those most likely to suffer spontaneous combustion are clergymen living by the seaside, but spontaneous combustion is by no means the same thing as lightning, and may have causes which are neither theological nor meteorological – a poor diet and excessive smoking for instance.

But it is not only prominent Christians who seem to be the targets of lightning bolts. Royalty seems to have been particularly vulnerable to lightning as well.

In January 1990 on her way to Mustique, Princess Margaret's British Airways 747 – it wasn't hers exactly, but a scheduled flight with Her Majesty on board – was struck by lightning and its nose cone damaged. The Duchess of York, five months pregnant, was travelling in a DC10 to Houston when that plane too was rocked by lightning. She 'admitted being nervous', but laughed and joked about it on arrival. Indeed as she toured the NASA space station she admitted that she would love to go into space and an official quipped: 'Consider yourself in the programme, Ma'am.' But perhaps she should think again. In 1969 Apollo 12's electrical system was disabled by lightning. In 1987 a flash struck an Atlas centaur rocket and destroyed it, while in the same year at Wallops, Virginia, three NASA rockets were launched prematurely after lightning struck. A rocket launch can trigger lightning from thunderstorms within a thirty-mile radius, which is worrying. With a princess or a pope on board the auguries would not be favourable.

You may be getting the impression that it is almost certain that you will be struck by lightning, and, if you are famous, inevitable. I must disabuse you. You are less likely to be struck by lightning than ever before. Far less. The worst accident attributable to a thunderstorm took place in Brescia, Italy, in 1769 when lightning struck the military arsenal, and 3,000 people were exploded and a sixth of the city destroyed. In the 1870s almost 50 Britons a year were killed by lightning and 300 a year in the US. The comparative figures now are 5 and 95. There is just as much lightning, 6,000 strikes a minute throughout the world. But farm labourers, who were the traditional targets, are thinner on the ground than they were a century ago, and in cities the proliferation of tall structures has diminished the chance of a six-foot male being struck. I say male advisedly. Eighty-five per cent of all lightning fatalities are male.

In Britain we average some 900 thunderstorms a year (out of some 16 million in the world), and most occur between May and September, with July and August the worst months. East Anglia and North Wales are the most vulnerable areas. A narrow strip of land, fifty miles long, south-west of the Wash and crossing into Leicestershire, is almost entirely free of thunder, which is as much a mystery to the Thunderstorm Census Organization of Huddersfield (from whom these statistics have been culled) as it is to me. An unexpected statistic confirms that each square mile of Britain is struck by lightning on average twice a year.

What is lightning? A high-voltage electrical discharge from cloud to cloud, or from cloud to ground. Why is there lightning? This is an altogether more difficult question to answer, and one which has not only baffled physicists for centuries, but continues to baffle them.

Below the ionosphere the air is electrically neutral. In a thundercloud lightning has a negative charge, and therefore leaves parts of the cloud positively charged. It is possible that hydrometeors, whirling particles of water or ice, collide with smaller particles and transfer their electrical charges. The larger particles become negatively charged and fall, while the smaller ones become positively charged and stay in the cloud. At least that is one theory, but it fails to account for a small positively-charged area regularly found at the base of a thundercloud (usually cumulo-nimbus with the sinister anvil shape).

Physicists explain this by citing a critical temperature of $-15°c$ at which negative charges become positive, and suggest that droplets in the lower portion of the cloud, growing warmer, become positive. In the highly volatile electrical field now existing within the cloud – volatile because there is a potential difference of between one and three million volts per metre – a lightning flash begins with an intermittent, branched discharge, called a 'stepped leader'. If this comes within 100 metres or so of the ground, leaving a trail of ionized air, it meets a powerful positive charge which rises to meet it. They join forces some fifteen metres above the ground. This 'return stroke' has a current of between 10,000 and 40,000 amperes. A second leader runs down the ionized channel left by the preceding return stroke, and so on. Typically a lightning flash may contain three or four leaders and return strokes, though ten times as many have been measured. Since the eye cannot register that there has been more than one 'flash', the lightning appears to flicker. Many of the branches of lightning fail to come close to the ground, and are short-lived and faint.

Within the lightning flash as it reaches the ground the heat is intense, as much as 30,000°c. The air expands and creates shock waves powerful enough to throw victims into the air, although it is more likely to tear their clothes off. These shock waves are the thunder. If lightning strikes an object containing liquid, the liquid boils, causing the object to explode, which is just what a tree does when blasted. Or the flash may strike sideways to a better conductor.

Light travels at 186,000 miles per second. Sound takes five

seconds to cover a mile. Consequently if you count the seconds between seeing the flash and hearing the thunder and divide by five you will get the distance you are from where the lightning has come to ground. It is unusual to be able to hear thunder at a distance greater than five miles.

The current physicists' explanation for thunder is pleasantly close to the explanation put forward by the Venerable Bede in the eighth century. Bede considered that lightning was caused by clouds rubbing together, and thunder by clouds banging together, but in medieval England, as in ancient Rome, the belief that lightning was a form of divine retribution was always to the fore. Just as Zeus sat in heaven with thunderbolts aimed at likely miscreants, so did God. This may have been because churches were so often struck by lightning; as the tallest buildings they were of course especially vulnerable. The more one venerated God the higher one built the church, and the higher one built the church the more likely God was to send a thunderbolt and knock it down again. It must have been perplexing. Parishioners were certainly perplexed and would ring the church bells to keep the anger of God at bay; the effect of this was that bell-ringing parishioners died regularly and unnecessarily when lightning was attracted down the damp and sweaty bell-ropes.

A breakthrough took place in 1752 when Benjamin Franklin used a weather-kite to establish that lightning constituted powerfully contained electricity. A spark from a thundercloud in which he was flying his kite travelled down the damp silk thread and jumped to a metal key. He took to storing his lightning in Leyden jars. Franklin made known the results of his experiment to the Royal Society – they made him a member – and promoted the use of pointed lightning conductors. George III was suspicious of the upstart American and, assuming that pointed conductor rods were obscurely connected with the American republicans, demanded blunt-ended ones for Buckingham Palace.

The debate about the most efficient design for lightning conductors rumbled on for many years, and still rumbles on.

Does a sharp bend in a conductor allow the lightning to escape? There are still scientists who believe so.

The fondness of lightning for computer networks is of contemporary concern. On numerous occasions computers have been knocked out by lightning flashes; the indifference of computer companies to the problem might be linked to the need for a burnt-out computer to be replaced by a new one! Patients in hospital beds linked to electrical systems are also especially vulnerable, but those most at risk are sports participants, and especially golfers. I have been singed on the wrist on the undulating fairway of the seventeenth at Temple Golf Club near Henley (the best line is as far to the left as you dare to go while avoiding the out of bounds. The green is then within easy reach of a well-struck second) and suffered a tingling sensation for some hours afterwards.

This is not my only close encounter with electrical storms. At our Broadstairs prep school we boys seemed to suffer more than our fair share of violent storms. The worst was the one which ripped the roof off the cottage rented by Mr Williams, the music master, leaving him and his wife exposed to the elements. We found what we took to be a thunderbolt on the cricket pitch the following day, but the headmaster told us it must be a small meteorite. Other boys in their dormitories told tales of balls of fire which had floated mysteriously past their beds, stories which I dismissed as typical schoolboy exaggerations. Now I'm not so sure.

Ball lightning takes various forms. It varies in size from a large apple to a small beach ball and in colour from red to orange to yellow. It may have a corona, it may emit sparks, it may crackle or hiss, it may smell of sulphur, and it sways as it travels, usually against the wind, although it is just as likely to be observed indoors as out. It often appears to eye-witnesses as though it is 'looking for something', which could be a radiator, a pipe, or an iron trivet. In due course it self-combusts or disappears through an open window or up a chimney.

Paul Davies, the author of *Fireball* and something of an expert on these phenomena, tells of a Smethwick housewife who was assaulted in her kitchen by a provocative fireball but courageously sent it packing, and suffered nothing more serious than a burnt frock.

These fireballs usually occur when there is electrical activity in the vicinity, but fair weather fireballs are not unknown. They are powerful little things. One fireball, a little more than twenty centimetres in diameter, anxious perhaps to be taken seriously, appeared in front of Roger Jennison, a professor of physical sciences at Kent University, floating down the centre aisle of Eastern Airlines flight EA 539 over New York City. The fireball was whitish blue and travelled quite slowly at waist height.

It was Professor Jennison, feeling no doubt that he had a personal interest in such matters, who submitted a video tape which an amateur cameraman had recorded during a thunderstorm to *Nature*. This showed what is believed to be the first example of ball lightning to be captured on film. It was shaped like an overinflated tyre with ridged edges, and this apparently was significant because if the ball had been a perfect sphere it could not have been created by magnetic forces. Professor Jennison's theory is that ball lightning consists of 'high frequency radio waves operating at about a billion cycles a second . . . and wrapped up in a tangle of energy.'

Many physicists have attempted to create fireballs artificially in laboratories with varying success. Pyotr Kapitza, a Russian physicist and Nobel Prize winner, identified them as resulting from superconducting ionized gas, caught up in an intense magnetic field. Others believe that fireballs are particles of dirt thrown up and charged by lightning strikes.

Recently Geert Dijkhuis, a Dutch scientist funded by the Rotterdam City Council, suggested that these little balls of fire are so powerful that they could be usefully used as a new source of energy generation. Rather than sitting around waiting for one though, one would have to manufacture them.

The wildest explanation comes from David Ashby and Colin

Whitehead of the Culham Lightning Studies Unit, which is part of the UK Atomic Energy Authority. They believe that fireballs might consist of tiny specks of anti-matter from outer space. I hope that they are wrong. The possibility that anti-matter might find its way into the earth's atmosphere is alarming, because when anti-matter meets matter, gamma rays are released, and one would do well to keep severely out of the way.

Ashby and Whitehead are not – so far as I know – nuts. If they were nuts, it seems unlikely that they would be working for the Atomic Energy Authority. But ever since Benjamin Franklin, thunderstorms have fascinated eccentrics.

There is Mr Elephigio Chikwana from Harare. He is a spiritual healer who urgently follows any reports of lightning strikes. He goes into a trance, turns the earth with a hoe where the strike landed, and uncovers the eggs of a giant bird which he claims flies in on the lightning blast. It seems probable that only Mr Chikwana has actually seen the eggs of the Mabanganana bird, but he knows that they have powerful properties, since they can attract bolts of lightning, no matter where they may be placed. Mr Chikwana does a roaring trade, because thunderstorms are especially frequent in Zimbabwe, and rural Zimbabweans tend to roof their huts with sheet metal.

More sinister was Nikola Tesla, a Yugoslav who invented Radar, worked on radio-controlled rockets twenty years before the first world war, and began building a broadcasting station on Long Island in 1900 with a grant from J. P. Morgan. He also developed an early version of the Star Wars defence project. It was Tesla's thesis that the earth is charged with electricity, and can be made to vibrate. It can also send electricity from place to place. Arriving in Colorado Springs, where the thunderstorms roar in across the Rockies, he built himself and John Jacob Astor, his latest patron, a factory for creating artificial lightning. By pumping charges into the earth and drawing them out again by means of upwards lightning, Tesla proved that it was possible to create a cheap and powerful supply of electricity. In a famous experiment he was able to illuminate 200 incandescent lamps at a distance of 26 miles.

Perhaps fortunately, Tesla was so eccentric in other ways – believing that he was the recipient of messages from outer space, for instance – that the implications of his discoveries were frequently ignored. Ignored that is, until 1977, when radio frequencies were disturbed and strange lights in the sky traced to Riga and Gomel, near Minsk. Sinister stories appeared in the papers suggesting that the Russians were developing some ideas of Tesla's in an effort to change the climate. Cold air, the rumours ran, was being diverted from Latvia and Leningrad to the North Atlantic coast of America.

Of course it was fashionable in 1977 to blame the Russians for everything, but the debate about using the weather as a weapon of war continues (see Chapter 11).

The latest experiments in fulminerology – not a pretty word but my own – are being conducted in France at ONERA, the national agency for aeronautic research. It monitors the radio signals which are released by thunderclouds through SAFIR, a computer programme, and can predict with some accuracy where lightning is most likely to strike, information of use to maintenance engineers on television transmitters, and rocket- launchers, among others. By using MINITEL, the electronic service available to all French telephone subscribers, French people can now track tropical storms across the country. If only Mr Chikwana could plug into MINITEL!*

What precautions should you take in thundery weather? You should avoid expanses of water, because if you are in or on water you are the highest thing in the vicinity. One of the effects of a powerful flash of lightning is to vaporize water. Some victims are found to have ruptured ear-drums and bowels as the fluids in their body violently expanded.

Clearly it's unintelligent to stand under a tree. It is not uncommon for a side-flash from a tree to be conducted onto somebody standing by the tree. But if you are determined to

* For other meteorological and climatic acronyms, see Appendix III.

stand under a tree, which tree should you choose? Says the country proverb:

> Beware of the oak, it draws the stroke.
> Avoid the ash, it courts the flash.
> Creep under the thorn, it will save you from harm.

Some research conducted in 1935 gave these particulars. Within the control area sixty-one oaks were struck, thirty-two elms, twenty-six ash trees, and thirteen poplars. The figures accorded closely with statistics from abroad. Beeches are relatively safe. But try not to stand under a tree at all. It would be best to try not to stand upright at all – worse still would be to *lie* under a tree; the voltage gradient along your body would be greater in a prone than in an upright position. To be on the safe side you should crouch with your feet together and your hands on your knees. Although this may be uncomfortable for long periods under a thorn bush, it is safe.

But if you avoid trees, are not open spaces equally risky? Well yes, they are. The safest place to be in a thunderstorm is indoors. Poor Jimmy Warren in our school dormitory did not think so, because in the fiercest of thunderstorms we would draw a pencil line from the metal window-frame to his metal bed-head and persuade him that lightning was powerfully conducted by lead. Poor Jimmy Warren!

Although you should not be swimming or water-skiing in a thunderstorm, you would do well to dunk yourself briefly in a nearby pond. Wet clothes will help to conduct the electricity along the length of your body and not through it. Rubber insulation is useful; motor-tyres have saved many lives; wellington boots too perhaps. So you are safer inside your car than you may think you are, but avoid touching any exposed metal parts.

If you are golfing, fishing or cricketing (in a tragedy at Isleworth in 1987 nine players were injured and one killed by side-flashes from a lightning strike), throw away your clubs, rods or bats, at the first sign of lightning. They can attract lightning, as, of course, umbrellas can. If a companion is struck and unconscious, first aid will often lead to a full recovery; and there are cases of people who have been paralysed, deaf and blind who have recovered the full use of their faculties after being struck by lightning – Frankenstein's monster too – so, as you see, every cloud has a silver lining.

6

The Pang and the Piddle in Peril

'Goodness comes out of people who bask in the sun, as it does out of a sweet apple roasted before the fire.'
Charles Dudley Warner (1871)

'Motorists faced hours of misery yesterday after part of the motorway surface began to crumble in the heat.' 'Ten thousand eggs which fell from a lorry began to fry on the road in the sizzling heat.'

The stories have become entirely predictable as each year produces its drought or heatwave or both. 1990 was regarded by many as the ultimate. I quote from the *Sunday Correspondent* for 5 August:

'As the hottest week in history ended yesterday, with Britain's seventy-nine-year-old temperature record broken by Cheltenham, Glos and Nailstone, Leics, the search for an explanation began.

'The 99°F (37°c) was followed by the hottest night since records began in 1941 with temperatures still at 82°F (28°c) at midnight in London.

'By 3 am the temperature had fallen only to 79°F (26°c) and it was still 75°F (24°c) at dawn.'

The hottest week in history? Well, maybe.

On 8 July 1707, for instance, men and horses collapsed and died of heatstroke during harvesting in England. The temperature then was estimated at 100°F, but that was the sort of round figure that would have been accepted.

This matter of the highest British temperature ever recorded is passionately argued. The estimable W. Marshall in *A Century of London Weather* records 100°F as having occurred at Greenwich on 9 August 1911 and adds: 'The reading is the all time record for London and the highest August temperature recorded anywhere in the British Isles', but along with 100.5°F (38.1°c – 22 July 1868, Tonbridge, Kent) and 99°F (37.2°c) at Greenwich (19 August 1932) it was recorded on a Glaisher screen and not on the officially approved Stevenson screen. Incidentally, C. E. Stevenson, the brilliant engineer who designed the screen, was Robert Louis's father. Compared with the Glaisher screen, computed for the thirty-five years from 1881 the Stevenson screen gave slightly lower (.3°F) maxima and slightly lower (.9°F) minima.

How are temperatures measured and just what is this Stevenson screen? An example may be seen in the weather enclosure in St James's Park. It appears as a cross between a beehive and a sound speaker, and contains maximum and minimum recording thermometers and 'dry bulb' and 'wet bulb' thermometers by means of which a relative humidity reading may be established. A curious effect of the current sophistication of information is that when Londoners read of anticipated high humidity they start to perspire.

An alternative to the Stevenson screen is a thermal radiation screen containing platinum electrical resistance thermometers. These can send information recorded automatically on a chart to the Bracknell Weather Centre, so they are ideal for isolated sites.

A word or two about the measuring of temperature. The problem is the need to record a variable factor in a constant way. The mercury thermometer, the bi-metallic spiral and the Bourdon tube were all quite satisfactory as portable self-recording instruments, but measuring air temperature is a complicated procedure. The intensity of the shade (in which, of course, all measurements are undertaken) is just a start. But where is the shade on an airport runway? And the shade, such as it is in the centre of a concrete shopping precinct, has little to do with the shade in a leafy meadow.

Bill, Michael and Ian enjoying a sunny interval but anticipating a shower.

Dramatic evidence in Maidstone of the force of the storm which swept across the southern counties during the night of 16 October 1987.

Left: A familiar scene on the morning after the big November 1987 storms. This felled giant was in Maidstone.

Opposite page, above: Emergency services? Mrs Joan Ricks of Abridge, Essex, attempts to make a connection from a callbox toppled by the storms of October 1987.

Opposite page, below: A public fund has been started to replace these historic oaks at Sevenoaks, Kent.

February 1990, floodwater in the north Wales village of Kinmel brings out a lifeboat.

Towyn in north Wales, the worst victim of the February 1990 flooding, but two residents at least are safe.

A waterspout by the pier at Yarmouth, Isle of Wight, 1987. All praise to the photographer who holds the camera steady.

Multiple auroral bands, one of the many sensational (and free) displays of the Northern Lights.

The Cray YMP 832 Supercomputer which ought to help the Met Office with their predictions. Its predecessor was a disappointing investment.

The bleak North East from rough Tartarian Shores
O'er Europe's Realms its freezing Rigour pours.
Stagnates the flowing Blood in Humane Vein
And binds the Silver Thames in Icy Chains.

FROST FAIR

Their usual Courses Rivulets refrain
And every Pond appears a Glassy Plain.
Streets now appear where Water was before
And Thousands daily walk from Shore to Shore.

Frost fairs have not occurred this century. Effluent from factories and power stations is more to blame than alleged global warming.

The drought at Church Stretton, Salop, 1976.

Hoaxers, hedgehogs, dust devils or aliens from outer space? Artistic certainly.

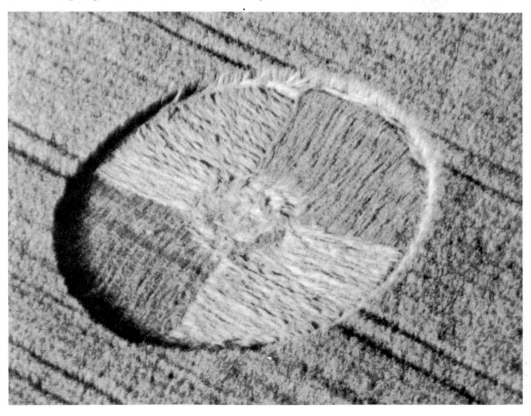

Ideally the temperature should be measured on a Stevenson screen set in a field of mown grass. Since caution should always be exercised when measuring extremes, these conditions will provide the most constructive, and therefore the most reliable, maxima. Sunshine is measured on a Campbell-Stokes Sunshine Recorder, an antique but dependable system which calculates the hours of sunshine from burn-marks left by the sun's rays on a calibrated card.

Even if the July 1707 temperature and the Greenwich and Tonbridge readings are discounted as Britain's maximum, can we accept 3 August 1990 as the hottest day ever recorded?

Until August 1990 the highest entirely authenticated record was 98°F (36.7°c) recorded at Canterbury, Epsom and Northants in August 1911. Professor Gordon Manley* estimates that 95°F (35°c) was exceeded in the Julys of 1757, 1808, 1825, and 1868. So it is almost certain that 100°F must often have been exceeded when there was either no satisfactory equipment to record the temperature or nobody at hand to notice (or both). But officially 3 August 1990 must stand. The summer of 1991 – indeed the whole of the year – was one of the warmest, although not quite as warm in Britain as 1989 or 1990. Internationally 1991 is regarded as the second hottest year on record.

It is interesting to look back briefly to the heatwave of 1911. The House of Lords was busy debating the Parliament Act, by which it was to reduce its own powers in favour of the Lower House. The debate was conducted in almost unendurable heat, and Lord Cromer wisely stayed away from the overcrowded chamber suffering from a sharp attack of gout.

There was a strike by transport workers and power cuts in Liverpool; riots followed. In London child mortality from diarrhoea and enteritis was a tragic consequence of the heat. More than 850 babies under two years of age died in the last week of August alone.

* *Climate and the British Scene* (Fontana, 1962)

According to the *Illustrated London News*:

'The swimming baths all round London did record business. The banks of the canals which cut through the East End were swarming with men and boys who braved even the upper layers of oil and dirt in their frantic quest for coolness. In the cafés and restaurants there were scenes such as are rarely witnessed. Men sat in shirt sleeves with their coats hung over the backs of their chairs, while at the railway stations half the male passengers in the trains which passed through were also in their shirt sleeves.'

1911 was also the year of the tragic Derby Day. Seventeen people and four horses were killed by lightning strikes on the Epsom Downs.

In other ways 1911 was exceptional. The heatwave continued with temperatures in the nineties for more than fifteen days and of the fine summers we have enjoyed recently only 1976 can compete. In that year there were also fifteen successive days with temperatures in the nineties, but these were all recorded in a single place.

What, speaking meteorologically, was happening during 1911 and those other breathless summers? A 'bollard' was what was happening. And what is a bollard? It is recently invented jargon for a blocking anti-cyclone.

The upper level prevailing westerly winds bifurcate, leaving a static high pressure area between them. Meandering low pressure areas around this anti-cyclone are not strong enough to make any inroads. The result is a sustained drought not just over England and Wales – Scotland often escapes the ravages of the heat – but over continental Europe as well. (The 1990 drought was just as devastating in France, Italy, and Greece as it was in England, although Spain experienced a wetter than average summer. August 1990 was quite a month in Tromso with temperatures in the upper twenties, unusual inside the Arctic Circle. In Alaska Seward broke all its records with 30°c while Fairbanks recorded 31°c.) Why are we bollarded? Meteorologists blame El Nino, but, as will become apparent throughout this book, they blame El Nino for much which they can't explain.

The modelmakers have succeeded in creating computer models of bollards, but have not been able to mimic their ability to plonk themselves down, like Giles's Grandmother on a picnic, and stay put. Dr Mike Hulme from the University of East Anglia's Climate Research Group is quite honest about it. 'I don't think we understand them as well as we'd like to. We're not clear why they are so prolonged, and equally we are not sure why they subside.' When meteorologists can establish the links between tropical and extra-tropical weather patterns, then perhaps they will be able to forecast bollards, and even, in time, discourage or avert them. But clearly not yet, not for a long time yet.

Overall, the spring of 1893 holds the record for the most significant drought. Seventy-three consecutive rainless days were recorded in East London during March, April and May. In the south of England, April and July are usually the driest months, January and December the wettest.

To a layman such as myself, all this goes to show that whenever newspapers trumpet another record-breaking temperature one should be healthily sceptical. In any case, a subject as wide-ranging as the climate has so many 'records' in so many categories that the only amazing thing would be if no records of any kind were broken anywhere in any year.

Records for warmth date back to 1659 and for sunshine to 1909. The hottest and sunniest months on record are as follows:

	Heat	Sunshine
January	1916	1959
February	1779	1949
March	1957	1929
April	1865	1914
May	1833	1989
June	1989	1957
July	1983	1911

August	1976	1975
September	1729	1911
October	1969	1959
November	1818	1989
December	1934	1962
Overall	1989	1989

There is no arguing that 1989 was exceptional. In Central England the mean temperature for the entire year was 51°F (10.6°c), 1.1°c above average.

Maximum and minimum temperatures are intriguing for the record-hunters, which means most of us. As a child I was far more interested in a maximum/minimum thermometer than I would have been in one which supplied an average temperature over twenty-four hours. But where climatologists are concerned it is the general shifts in temperature, represented by these 'mean annual figures', which are paramount.

When I worked in television, and now that I work in radio, I study the ratings with fascinated scepticism. I know only too well how careless scheduling, or freakish events over which broadcasters have little control, can affect a week's or even a month's ratings; but it is the trends that concern the programme controllers, the chief executives, the shareholders and the advertisers.

The weather has a habit of evening itself out – 'Be it dry or be it wet, the weather'll always pay its debt,' – and climatologists find very hot or very cold days no more interesting than a philatelist who can only acquire one of a set.

1989 and 1990 were glorious summers in Britain, hot and sunny, but can you recall others which followed sequentially? 1975 and 1976 were just as fine and just as hot. 1976 was exceptional if you take the three summer months (June, July and August). Only 1826 seems to have been hotter. The three driest years this century were 1902, 1921 and 1990.

Perhaps I should not talk so blithely of 'Britain'. From a fascinating chart prepared by the delightfully named M. O.

Bracknell, it appears that the average mean temperature for six British centres varies significantly. This is the comparison covering the typical period of 1941–70 inclusive. (The figures are centigrade.)

	J	F	M	A	M	J	J	A	S	O	N	D	O/A
Eastb'rne	4.5	4.5	6.3	8.8	11.8	14.7	16.6	16.8	15.3	12.3	8.2	5.9	10.5
Kew	4.2	4.5	6.6	9.5	12.6	15.9	17.5	17.1	14.9	11.6	7.5	5.3	10.6
Oxford	3.5	4.0	6.2	9.1	12.1	15.3	16.9	16.5	14.4	10.9	6.9	4.6	10.1
Sheffield	3.4	3.5	5.5	8.3	11.3	14.5	16.0	15.7	13.9	10.7	6.6	4.6	9.5
Morpeth	2.6	2.7	4.5	6.9	9.3	12.5	14.1	13.9	12.3	9.4	5.5	3.7	8.1
Braemar	0.4	0.5	2.7	5.2	8.2	11.5	12.7	12.3	10.3	7.5	3.4	1.7	6.4

The estimable Bracknell chart indicates that over the whole of this century up to 1970 and in each of these six centres, winters have been growing colder and summers hotter.

Overall the Twenties were notable for the heatwave of 1921 and the freeze-up of 1929. The Thirties enjoyed mild winters and fine summers in 1933 and 1934 (how often they seem to come in pairs!). The Forties and Fifties had generally savage winters and four glorious summers (1947, 1949, 1955 and 1959). The winter of 1962–3 was a wicked one indeed.

It is inadvisable to set too much store by those who speak nostalgically of the frosty winters and splendid summers of their youth. Ask them first whether they lived in town or country and whether or not they enjoyed the 'benefits' of centrally-heated houses.

There has been a mass movement from the country to the towns, and naturally in the country it is not unusual to go skating on a lake, to light a log fire or to throw snowballs at the vicar.

Nor does the commuter travelling from a centrally-heated house via air-conditioned Saab to temperature-controlled office take too much notice of a perfect summer's day beyond perhaps registering that the double-glazed windows are in serious need of cleaning and that the sales manager has damp patches under his enthusiastic arms.

But droughts affect everyone. The drought conditions of the

last three years have been more serious in some parts of the country than in others. In East Anglia December 1990 was officially declared to be the twenty-ninth successive month of drought. Buyers of spray irrigators received an earnest warning that they must not overstep the regulations which permitted them to take water from boreholes and rivers. Car-washing and garden- watering were discouraged if not entirely forbidden. (A drought, as defined by the London Weather Centre, is quite a paltry creature. Just fifteen consecutive days with less than 0.02 mm of rain.)

It is quite misleading for people to blame the long, hot, dry summers for shortage of water and hose-pipe bans. What happens during the winter is what affects our water reserves. Almost half our supplies come from underground sources; the remainder from reservoirs and rivers. Some parts of the country, the eastern strip from Yorkshire to Kent, rely on underground water for three quarters of their supply. And of course to the east of the Pennines the main crops are cereals and arables, while to the damper west of the Pennines the farmers concentrate more on livestock and pasture.

The driest place in England is claimed to be Lee Wick Farm near St Osyth, within a few miles of Clacton. Andrew and Robert Faulds, father and son, have kept conscientious records over more than thirty years and suggest an average rainfall of 20.2 inches. However, they have pumped up subterranean water and stayed in business as arable farmers, though not, in recent years, without difficulty. The message is clear. It is not what falls from the sky so much as how you conserve and distribute what you already have. And what does fall from the sky needs to fall at the right time, ideally in the spring for spring-sown cereals.

The richest underground reservoirs in Britain are the aquifers, sandstone basins in the Midlands and chalk beds in the south and east. They have been seriously depleted. A well on the Sussex Downs which has been continuously measured since 1836 has only been lower on four occasions. It is always possible to sink more boreholes, but that does not increase the amount of water available, just the speed with which it can be extracted. As the water in the aquifer falls the mineral contamination increases until eventually the water is unusable. Some of the water in these natural tanks is 20,000 years old and so salt that it has been useless for centuries. Rivers fed by underground springs also suffer when too much is taken through boreholes. The National Rivers Authority has recently issued warnings for many rivers including six which supply the Thames region, the Pang, the Ver, the Misbourne, the Wey, the Darent and Letcombe Brook. The Darent is now in a critical decline. The situation in Hampshire, Wiltshire and Dorset is little better, the Upper Avon, the Wylie, the Nadder and the Bourne being highly vulnerable along with the trout streams, the Allen and the Piddle. Beautiful names for beautiful streams, yet as the flow diminishes the algae move in and a noxious blue-green slime spreads over the sparkling waters. The fish go, and the vegetation of the banks. Then the birds that feed off the fish and nest in the vegetation.

One of the results of a prolonged drought is to create a sort of Stephen King atmosphere. In the summer of 1990 weaver fish with poisonous spikes hovered off the coast of Wales, and scarlet worms an inch or two long invaded a children's paddling pool in Cleethorpes. A cache of stolen antique weapons was spotted when the level of the Thames fell at Eton, and a life-size waxwork of a medieval knight melted into a greasy mess at Stanstead Montfichet Castle in Essex. Several ghost villages emerged eerily from dried-up reservoirs including Mardale at Haweswater and Ashopton from the Ladybower Reservoir in the Peak District.

Dust-devils, caused by high temperatures and light winds, swirled around all over the place, including – improbably – Surbiton. Pig-farmers coated their pigs in suntan oil to stop them overheating. Sunflowers went out of control in Berkshire and turned into triffid-like monsters. The International Worm-Charming Festival in Devon was marred by the hard ground.

Only forty worms were charmed to the surface in twenty minutes against a world record of 149. Dowsers enjoyed a marvellous summer. So did wasps, cockroaches, bees, ladybirds, and butterflies. The Tiggywinkle Hedgehog Hospital in Aylesbury was frantically busy rehydrating hedgehogs, and a yuppie who beat the hose-pipe ban by washing his precious car with Perrier water must have been choked when he read that Perrier had been taken to task for impurities in their product. Dirty water from the penguin pool at Newquay Zoo was used to sprinkle the corporation putting green. Things became really desperate in the Scilly Isles. Attempts to ship in fresh water in the ballast tanks of the ferry Scillonian III foundered when the water was found to be contaminated with sea-salt. At the end of its tether the Council approved a slogan which read, 'Don't Blush, Don't Flush the Toilet Every Time.'

The problem is the same with drought as with snow. In our temperate climate it is quite uneconomic to provide for extremes. Occasionally we get an earth-tremor, and it would be perfectly possible to set up a round-the-clock Earthquake Watch. It is not beyond the bounds of belief that some lives might one day be saved as a result, but only the Monster Raving Loony Party would advocate such a policy. We have had four notable droughts since the last war, rather less than one per decade. It is not unreasonable to live with stand-up pipes and hose-pipe bans one summer in ten.

With the privatization of water the economic situation has changed. It has been well known for years that our antiquated pipe systems permit between 25 per cent (Thames Water) and 32 per cent (South-West Water) of our valuable supplies to seep away and evaporate. If only the water companies are long-sighted enough to invest some of their income in new pipes, huge improvements are sure to follow. North-West Water announced that an £8.5 million of 'Leakage Control' would save £120 million of 'New Supply Facilities'.

If money were no object our ultimate goal should be a National Water Grid. Washing machines, dishwashers, garden sprinklers, and second cars lead to an endless escalation in the demand for more and more water. Flushing the toilet uses two gallons of water, showering yourself and washing up a meal for four people, five gallons each, taking a bath, thirty, using an automatic washing machine, forty, and running the garden hose-pipe for an hour, 200 gallons. As affluence increases, depletion of the supplies is likely to continue even with normal rainfall in the next few years – 1991 was encouragingly normal. Yet Scotland and the North-West never suffer from water shortage and could supply the rest of us in times of need, though the grid would be colossally expensive. Water cannot be compressed and is heavy to move.

Thames Water has already started construction of an eighty-kilometre Water Ring Main below London. Linking the Thames and the Lee Valley, half of the capital's needs will be met from this new resource. The success of the Ring Main – and how can it fail? – may persuade other urban centres to invest in a similar scheme, in which case a nationwide grid may become a possibility after all. The short-term solution is metering.

From the year 2000 domestic rates will no longer be the basis for water charges, and a fairer system, probably based on water meters, will be introduced by the companies. Where metering has been sample-tested, a saving of 10 per cent overall was achieved.

The largest testing area in a massive project undertaken in 1989 was the Isle of Wight. Residents who had endured discomfort during the installation of the meters were even more discomfited when they discovered that the increased charges in some households amounted to 400 per cent, although those living on their own benefited.

Under the present system the water companies make more profit the less water they supply. Under metering the reverse would be the case, so that one would expect them to do all they could to encourage profligacy, raising prices in times of drought, but reinvesting profits in new equipment. If the profits justified it, a national grid could then become a reality. Meanwhile we must tolerate the inconvenience, putting a half-brick in the lavatory cistern and comforting ourselves that statistically we can expect fewer long, hot summers in the next decade. We might also console ourselves by reflecting that Harrods will never run out of water. It has two artesian wells of its own.

7

. . . .

The London Particular

'The fog comes
on little cat feet.
It sits looking
over the harbour and city
on silent haunches
and then moves on.'

Carl Sandburg, *Fog* (1916)

I was having a driving lesson in Henley in thick fog. It was 1955 – three years after the most serious pollution disaster in the history of the world – and a year before the passing of the Clean Air Act. The only way to stay on the road was to drive within sight of the rear-lights of the car in front. Eventually the car in front drew to a halt and a large but genial man climbed out and strolled to the driver's window of my car.

Through the swirling mist I was just able to make out that we were in the elegant driveway of a country house. 'I don't know about you,' he said, 'but I live here.'

There were many such stories. Ernie Hill was at the wheel of his No. 2 bus in the 1952 peasouper when he reached Hyde Park Corner, and came to a halt as the double-decker bus climbed the first few steps outside the front entrance of the old St George's Hospital.

'This policeman sticks his head through my window and says: "Ere, where do you think you're going?" I told him I thought I was in Park Lane. "Another few yards mate," he said, "and you'll be in the operating theatre".'

That weekend of 5 December 1952 remains in the memory of all who survived it. Four thousand didn't. And those 4,000 may now be seen to have been martyrs in a worthwhile cause, for the 'Killer Smog', as it came to be known, led directly to a 1953 Committee on Air Pollution, and the Committee's deliberations led to the Clean Air Act of July 1956.

There was powerful opposition to the act. Harold Macmillan, who was the Conservative Minister with responsibility for such matters, twice ruled out legislation. 'An enormous number of broad economic considerations have to be taken into account', he told the House, and the Health Minister, Iain Macleod, supported him. But the Committee of Inquiry's conclusion could not be gainsaid. Air pollution was costing between £200 million and £300 million a year; it would cost a tiny sum to clear up the air. Gerald Nabarro pressed for action, and four years after that nightmare weekend, the bill was law.

It had not been a recent problem, and had not been caused, as many believed, by the Industrial Revolution. On the contrary, both Edward I and Elizabeth I had inveighed against the burning of coal, though only when Parliament was in session. John Evelyn suggested to Charles II that something should be done about the 'Catharrs, Phthisicks, Coughs and Consumptions (which) rage more in this one City, than in the Whole Earth besides.' Charles II remained unconvinced.

Throughout Victorian London the situation deteriorated. Who can read Dickens's novels without a powerful sense of what it must have been like in those gloomy, lawless streets during a 'London Particular'?

By the end of the century, it was recorded that the number of foggy days per year had increased from an average of nineteen to fifty-five. (Technically, fog is said to occur if visibility is less than 1,000 metres; thick fog means visibility is down to 200 metres or less.)

The November of 1901 was regarded by many Londoners as bringing in the most impenetrable fog ever known in the capital. In the East End some residents reported that they could not even see their own feet and had the uncanny feeling that they were floating in space. There were significant London fogs in 1930 when there were several reports of people walking into rivers and canals and drowning. In 1947 the fog was blamed for a series of train crashes. The traditional semaphore-type signals were positioned so high up their poles and were lit so dimly that stories abound of crews being forced to climb up the poles to determine whether they should proceed or delay.

But none of those can hold a candle to the greatest peasoupers of December 1952 and December 1962. There were so many chemicals floating around in the stagnant air during that long, endless, weekend in December 1952 that the air turned a dirty yellow-grey. People wore smog-masks, and seemed like figures from some science fiction film of the remote future. Bus conductors walked in front of their buses; bus-travellers stayed in their unheated buses when the transport could finally proceed no further. A blind man in Notting Hill guided people to their houses. Visibility was less than five yards throughout the city. On the Sunday night it became, officially, 'nil'.

The following evening the audience at Sadlers Wells – those who had been intrepid enough to make the journey – could no longer see the stage. The performance had to be cancelled after the first act. A cattle-truck bringing potential prizewinners to Smithfield took seven hours over the journey from Paddington to Earl's Court. Nothing comparable had ever been experienced before.

The Clean Air Act of 1956 which created smokeless zones in the centres of our cities has been a success. But not an unmitigated success. In 1957 the Lewisham rail disaster with eighty-seven fatalities resulted from smog. On several evenings in 1959 a strange phenomenon could be observed outside Swiss Cottage Underground station. A posse of students with flaming torches would round up passengers emerging into the fog, instruct them to cling onto the coat of the person in front, and announce, 'Adelaide Road and all points east!' As each intersection was reached, the name of the subsidiary road would be announced, and those who lived in it would scuttle off into invisibility.

And in 1962, exactly ten years after the smog to end all smogs, another disastrous peasouper infected the capital with 5,000 buses unable to continue. Charlie Grognet, bus conductor, promised to get the five remaining passengers of his No. 2 home if they would take it in turns to walk in front of the bus and light the way. They responded in true British fashion, as Charlie reported: 'I was exhausted, covered in grime, and I hadn't even had a chance to collect their fares. To my disgust they all shrank down in their seats and said "no". So I chucked the lot of them off!'

But the success of the Clean Air Acts may be gauged from these statistics: at Kew the average annual frequency of fogs between 1934 and 1943 was thirty-four days per annum. From 1964 to 1973 it fell to fourteen days per annum. The comparative figures for Greenwich were forty-one days and eight days. Now, of course, the use of natural gas in domestic heating and process industry is even more significant.

I have been emphasizing London, but the problem is by no means confined to the capital. For ten days in November 1936, Manchester suffered continuous thick fog. Here the soot deposit was such that a loathsome black slime coated everything, and conditions were not much better in Birmingham. Silver and copper artefacts were black within an hour or two of cleaning. Rain which finally fell on the twenty-sixth of the month was recorded as having over Bournville a hydrogen-ion concentration of three – alarmingly acid. It calls to mind a touch ruefully the words of the mayor of Middlesbrough when in the 1880s he opened the portentous town hall with these words, 'Smoke is an indication of plenty and work (applause) – an indication of prosperous times (cheers) that all classes of people are employed (cheers). Therefore we are proud of our smoke (prolonged cheers).'

Dublin has had a fog problem for at least 300 years. In 1729 Dean Swift inveighed against the fog and its effects on poor people. In January 1982 a figure of 1,800 micrograms per cubic metre was reported in the Dublin smog. This figure was more than seven times the European agreed maximum of 250 micrograms. A sardonic cartoon in the *Irish Times* commented: 'On the plus side it makes it impossible to see the sewage flowing into Dublin Bay . . .'

The cities of Central Europe have been impregnated over the last half century with a particularly discouraging and sour smell, which is attributable to the brown coal burnt in the power stations and exacerbated in what was East Germany by the 'stinking trabbies' or Trabant cars. The German government has been active in its anti-pollution policies, promising to halve sulphur dioxide emissions by 1995, and banning private motoring in Berlin when there is an official smog alert.

Since unification it has become clear that the pollution problems of the old East Germany, which successive leaders denied or ignored or both, are Germany's problems, Europe's problems. The lesson of Chernobyl is a lesson for us all.

Paris suffers the same disease; the Eiffel Tower is uniquely able to monitor smog pollution over the city but Paris not infrequently exceeds the sulphur dioxide limits, with Parisians being encouraged to lay off driving, jogging and cigarette smoking until conditions improve.

It appears that the neologism 'smog' was first used in London in 1905 by the honorary treasurer of the Coal Smoke Abatement Society. Later in Los Angeles an inebriated reporter confused the words smoke and fog and his editor joyously celebrated the discovery of a potent headline.

Los Angeles smog is now, of course, a favourite tourist attraction. Additionally it has been established at the Beltsville Agricultural Research Centre in Maryland that the Los Angeles smog contains suspended significant quantities of pesticides and other toxic compounds. The city has three stages of smog alert. In the first stage, normal precautions, such as smog masks, are recommended, in the second, industry has to curtail its activities and companies employing more than 100 people must invoke carpooling programmes. In the third stage alert businesses and industries have to close and residents remain at home. To my knowledge there has not yet been a third stage alert in Los Angeles.

Smog in the Grand Canyon is an increasing problem with blame being laid partly at the door of pollution-bearing winds from Los Angeles, and more immediately at a Navajo generating station some seventy miles away in Page, Arizona. Most other national parks are similarly concerned.

The most dangerous city in the world for smog is Mexico City, 7,000 feet above sea level. Ironically, the valley of Mexico, in which the capital is located, was described by Cortes when he first set eyes on it in the sixteenth century as 'the most transparent zone' he had ever seen. But now atmospheric contamination has turned the air to the colour of chocolate. Eighty per cent of the contamination is thought to come from the city's three million cars, while it appears that the state-owned oil monopoly, Petroleos Mexicanos, has just added a paraffin-based detergent, probably a carcinogen, to its petrol.

Since the Clean Air Acts the worst of the fogs seem to be over, and yet, when there is a fog, the results are desperate. 'Motorway madness' shriek the headlines with yet more quotes from harassed police officers claiming that motorists are driving too fast and too close together. I no longer accept this. There are some motorists who are recklessly selfish or so personally inadequate as to need to prove themselves at speeds in excess of what is sensible, but most have little desire to be burned alive in their vehicles and display a sensible knowledge of the hazards of motorway driving in the fog. It is not as if they haven't been told.

It seems far more likely that drivers in fog suffer a form of sensory deprivation. In normal conditions the motorway driver is taking in a mass of stimuli. He or she notices the changing traffic patterns, the drivers of other vehicles, road signs, the countryside, and features of particular interest. In fog there is nothing to look at but the road ahead.

Astronauts undergoing training are required to spend some hours floating in water, deprived of all external stimuli. No wonder that after an average of two hours they begin to hallucinate. So, to a lesser degree, do drivers in fog.

Furthermore, just as in a glider when one runs into a thermal within a cloud one has no awareness of altitude, so the driver has no appreciation of speed. It is also possible that a fear of being run into by a driver behind may cause a driver to increase speed, and since he or she can see nothing ahead, the subconscious assumption is that there can be nothing ahead. Noise is muffled, and with no sense of speed the driver's ability to estimate braking distances is seriously affected. Objects seen with peripheral vision seem smaller, and in fog appear further away than they really are. It is not 'motorway madness' we are dealing with here, but motorway hallucination and sensory deprivation.

Imagine a line of cars travelling at 70 mph and separated by 140 feet – or ten cars' breadths – from the one in front. Imagine further that the leading car encounters an immovable object 140 feet from its front bumper. Its driver applies average maximum braking – 21.5 feet per second – after an average reaction time – 0.7 seconds – and so do all the other cars. Inevitably the first five cars would run into each other. If the speeds are reduced to 65 mph and the distance 120 feet instead of 140 feet, there would be a pile-up of six cars. And so on . . .

The *Highway Code* states that at 70 mph the shortest braking distance is 315 feet, or 22½ car lengths, but in fog this could often be beyond the range of visibility. The consequences are inevitable.

What can be done? Fog sensors on motorways may help, and electronic equipment giving safe distance/speed ratios for motorway driving in all cars would certainly help, but it is vital to explain to drivers what happens to them in fog, rather than castigating them in general terms and waiting for the next catastrophe. When conditions are sufficiently ominous, motorways should be closed.

Clearly the United Kingdom is never going to be free of fog. By a nicely-timed irony the newly established 'All-Weather' horse-racing track at Southwell was no sooner opened than it was closed as a result of fog in November 1989. And the 'Killer Smogs' will return whenever there is enough pollution in the atmosphere to create them. Bonfire night in 1987 helped to create a porridge out of an honest-to-goodness fog. A thick fog blurred central and suburban London for several days in November 1991. But it seems likely that increasingly in the future it will be the bricks, concrete and tarmac of the city centres which will be free of fog, since these surfaces cool more slowly than the leafy suburbs, and the commuter residential areas which will be rime-encrusted and fogbound.

8

· ·

Let it Come Down

'Rain is good for vegetables, and for the animals who eat those
vegetables, and for the animals who eat those animals.'
Samuel Johnson (6 July 1763)

Wisden is the best meteorological record of Britain's disappointing summers. 1923 and 1924 were years for sitting
in the pavilion and musing on great performances of the past;
1930 and 1931 were little better; 1936, 1948 and 1950 were
washouts, and 1983, well it scarcely bears thinking about. But
one needs to keep things in proportion. If you tried to play
cricket, for instance, on the slopes of Mount Wai-'ale-'ale in
Hawaii (let alone pronounce it) you might long for a touch of Old
Trafford. 460 inches of rain fall annually on Mount Wai-'ale-'ale,
and taking the year as a whole there are just thirty days without
rainfall. You would be well advised to fly your teams urgently to
Arica in Chile, for there the annual rainfall is said to be a mere 0.8
of a millimetre, although how such a dribble can be accurately
measured defeats me.

London's annual rainfall is about twenty-four inches. (It may
be unhelpful to speak about 'an inch of rain' without giving
some idea of just what that signifies. Imagine a day of steady
rain, a good old-fashioned British soaking over twenty-four
hours without a break. That would be approximately an inch.)
The wettest place in the British Isles is Snowdon in Wales – about
seven times wetter than London – followed by Blackwater Dam
in Scotland, three times wetter than London. The driest places
are all to the east of the country, places such as York, Doncaster,
and Ipswich. In London the wettest month is August, the driest
February, March and April. Manchester can expect to suffer

about thirty-four more rainy days in a year than London. In 1928 Styehead, in what was then Cumberland, received 250 inches of rain. In 1921 only ten inches fell on Margate.

In London the two wettest years were 1852 and 1903. In 1852 the bulk of the rain fell between August and November. In 1903 it was scarcely dry at all. 1915, 1924 and 1927 were all wet. The heaviest London downpour occurred on 16 June 1917 with 4.65 inches of rain on Kensington in less than two and a half hours, although the record British rainfall for a single day was eleven inches (279 millimetres) at Martinstown, Dorset, on 18 July 1955, followed by 9.56 inches in Somerset on 18 June 1917. 1921 was exceptionally dry. The summer of 1959 produced a drought in parts of eastern England of fifty-seven days (14 August – 9 October). 1947, which seemed to me, as a tiny boarder at a prep school on the Isle of Thanet, a succession of hot and cloudless summer days, had already suffered severe flooding in March and a very wet June.

Despite the floods of 1990, of which more later, and the drenching June of 1991, the last few years have been drier than average. But attitudes have not changed. Our largely urban population still complains whenever it rains. It talks of barbecues and lying on the beach; it has forgotten that once we used to pray for rain.

> We plough the fields and scatter
> The good seed on the land,
> And it is fed and watered
> By God's almighty hand.

Well, *we* don't plough or scatter. And we no longer welcome the rain as a benison, as an assurance that we are divinely nurtured, if not by God's almighty hand, then at least by the North Atlantic Drift and a series of depressions from the Azores. So protected do we feel that only 29 per cent of the population wear waterproof clothing, and only 10 per cent admit to owning an umbrella. We laugh and joke a little unfairly about the

dampness of our climate, but we take not the slightest precautions to keep ourselves dry. Odd.

Few of us have experienced serious flooding. We should
thank our lucky stars that we have not.

At 2.30 am on 26 February 1990, the Storm Tide Warning
Service, part of a national system known inevitably as Operation
Neptune, issued an alert. At least it was to claim later that it had.
Tidal surges which could be as high as 16.22 metres should be
anticipated between nine and eleven that morning in the area of
Towyn. The alert was never received in Towyn, according to the
technical services director of the borough council. It would
probably not have made much difference, although the unfortunate residents of that rather ramshackle bit of West Wales might
have been evacuated with rather more dignity.

At 11.40 am a stretch of some 300 metres of the Towyn sea-
wall was swept away and nearly 3,000 properties in Towyn,
Kinmel Bay and Pensarn were inundated. Harold was walking
his dog up Sandbank Road when seawater with the force of an
army convoy swept his feet from under him. 'I just prayed the
traffic lights would be red when I reached the main road because
I knew I wouldn't be able to stop,' he recalled wryly.

Nobody was drowned in the Towyn floods, although there
were several deaths in other parts of the country. A local GP
suggested that as many as ten people could have died from
flood-related trauma. Traumatic it must have been. Your food
rots, untreated sewage backs up and overflows from your cess
pit, your front lawn is piled high with soggy detritus. Very little
can be salvaged. Best china is smashed, best clothes are useless,
family photographs are indecipherable. Think for a moment of
your most treasured possessions, and now imagine what they
would be like if left to float in foul-smelling mud and water for
several days. When the flood water has permeated the founda-
tions of the property, the house itself may be beyond salvage.

Mr and Mrs Stilsted, retired pensioners, had to move into their
garage. Mr Stilsted said, 'A few weeks after we were flooded out,
with sewage covering everything in the house, I went to the

social security office. I explained we needed urgent assistance. They offered me £15 . . . The gas board charged me £69 for a new meter. We kept getting final demands for our Poll Tax bill for £522.'

Mr Derrick Overthrow's market garden business was wiped out. 'I have had a good cry this morning,' he reported as he assessed the full extent of his losses, 'I don't think I have cried for forty years.'

Some residents of Towyn remained blackly humorous in spite of everything. 'It had not really hit us until Charles and Di came round,' said a man in a wheelchair who had not been able to afford insurance for the contents of his home, 'then we knew we were headlines, and really, really in trouble.' But ten weeks after the floods the Secretary of State for Wales announced that those whose houses had not been insured would have the full cost of structural repairs met by the government.

As a result of the Towyn floods property insurance premiums have been increased on many low-lying properties. But since water now belongs to water companies and their shareholders and no longer to God, it is hard to understand how river flooding can any longer be considered acts of God. If rivers overflow their banks, those who suffer should be able to sue the appropriate company. They might just win.

A month after the Towyn floods receded, experts investigating the silt remaining around the town found it to be contaminated by radioactivity some ten times higher than the safety limits set by the government. The americum and plutonium infecting the debris was thought to have originated in Sellafield.

But the Towyn floods, disastrous as they certainly were for the inhabitants, are of little consequence when set against some of the massive floods of the past or the anticipated floods which many believe global warming will bring (see chapter 13).

Jean Ingelow wrote a poignant ballad in the last century about a high tide on the coast of Lincolnshire, but 1953 was the year of the worst ever East Anglian floods. On 1 February storm winds combined with a particularly high tide to flood a quarter of a million acres. Many lives were lost.

The Lynton/Lynmouth disaster is deeply entrenched in the collective subconscious. I was being driven through Devon and Cornwall on the evening of 13 August 1952. We were on our way to Mullion. It rained with good old-fashioned persistence all day. It was only the following morning that we heard about the tragic effects of what to us had been a dismally damp start to our summer holiday. The East and West Lyn rivers had burst their banks and had hurtled down the precipitous hill. Rocks and boulders were dragged through houses and hotels. 130 cars were swept out to sea. More than thirty people died. In those days nobody knew about such things as 'flood-related trauma', so no records were kept. People became depressed as a result of losing everything, and never 'rallied round'. It was as simple and tragic as that. But how quickly we forget! Ask people at the office or supermarket or club what they remember of the Lynton/Lynmouth floods, whether anybody was drowned and if so how many. They will have only the vaguest recollections. Even the memory of Aberfan begins to fade . . .

Britain often endures floods. In 1967 nearly six inches of rain fell over Great Langdale in twenty-four hours. Over ten inches of rain fell over western Scotland in two days the following year, and 1968 also saw downpours over southern England with Guildford under water on 16 September. Violent storms are extremely localized, of course, and it is hard to establish authentic records. But we do know that in Hampstead seventeen centimetres of rain fell in just three hours on 14 August 1975. Almost within a stone's throw of Hampstead, the London Weather Centre recorded little more than a trace of rain.

I love the rain in London. I never wear a waterproof coat and never carry an umbrella, and only get severely drenched once or twice a year. It is always possible to find shelter from the rain in a London street. Puddles thrown up by passing cars and buses are more of a problem. But rain is not unpleasant; one doesn't need to be Gene Kelly or in love – or both – to appreciate its finer points. I agree with Chiang Lee, a Chinese visitor to Britain, when he wrote, 'I walked on and on in the rain, smiling and making friends with the particles of mist as they touched my face . . . I hardly noticed that my clothes were quickly becoming soaked through; I was happy in the rain and preferred the misty mountains and trees.'

9

The Wrong Sort of Snow

'Snow is all right while it is snowing;
It is like inebriation because it is very
pleasing when it is coming, but very
unpleasing when it is going.'

Ogden Nash, *Jangle Bells* (1938)

It was in the middle of the seventeenth century that Fellows of the Royal Society realized the importance of recording the weather. What is the point of living through memorable times if nobody will remember them? 'I was there, I lived through it, and here is the proof . . .' You would be unlucky if, having gone to great lengths to record the weather, you then found yourself living through unexceptional times. You would be doubly unlucky if, when the exceptional came along, your equipment was not up to recording it.

It is proper for scientists and scientific journals to be sceptical of new theories and broken records. They require panels of experts to analyse the statistics before proceeding to publication. It has been known for these experts to dismiss the evidence out of hand if it conflicts with the theories which made them famous, or to adapt the evidence to dignify or substantiate their own research.

There may be political reasons for faking evidence. Trophim Denisovitch Lysenko was a Russian agriculturalist and geneticist. His dubious results were accepted by the Soviet establishment who considered Mendelism incompatible with dialectical materialism. In Britain J. B. Haldane, a Communist sympathizer, supported Lysenko on ideological grounds and against his better judgement.

Politics talks. Money shouts. In the notorious and farcical case of the Hitler diaries good money had been paid out in order that the diaries should be genuine. The truth became almost irrelevant. The desire for profit is a powerful aphrodisiac, exceeded only in the case of scientists by the desire for fame. The extreme example of Donald Crowhurst is superbly ironic. Crowhurst went to extraordinary lengths to convince the world that he had circum-navigated the globe. Deranged by failure he killed himself and acquired far more celebrity than if he had sailed sweetly and courteously around the world.

I have gone to some lengths to show how sceptical we need to be when scientists make extravagant claims and when their evidence cannot easily be substantiated. The clergymen and country doctors who recorded the weather for the Royal Society in the seventeenth and eighteenth centuries may have been over-enthusiastic on occasion. But their findings were based on primitive instruments, often home-made.

So when journalists or forecasters write so blithely and speak so airily of 'the hottest day since . . .' or 'the coldest winter since . . .' or 'that notable April of 1712 when . . .', one should listen politely but with a large salt-cellar to hand.

I would like to draw your attention to the work of the late Professor Gordon Manley, who collated so many of these amateur historic records. Manley's technique was to take the records for four separate centres in the Midlands and average them out. According to him the coldest winter on record was the winter of 1683–4, the year of one of the longest lasting of the frost fairs, which were frequently held on the Thames, especially in the seventeenth and eighteenth centuries. I quote John Evelyn's diary entry for 24 January 1684:

> The frost continuing more and more severe, the Thames before London, was still planted with boothes in formal streetes, all sorts of trades and shops furnish'd and full of commodities, even to a printing presse, where the people

and ladyes tooke a fancy to have their names printed, and the day and yeare set down when printed on the Thames: this humour tooke so universally, that 'twas estimated the printer gain'd £5 a day, for printing a line onely, at sixpence a name, besides what he got by ballads, etc. Coaches plied from Westminster to the Temple, and from several other staires, to and fro, as in the streetes, sleds, sliding with skeetes, a bull-baiting, horse and coach races, puppet-plays, and interludes, cookes, tipling, and other lewd places, so that it seem'd to be a bacchanalian triumph, or carnival on the water.

At least in the seventeenth century people knew how to enjoy their cold winters; all we seem able to do is complain about late trains.

Enjoy it they did, but suffered too. From the parish register of St Bartholomew at Ubley comes this record of that wicked winter of 1684:

The ground was not open nor the snow cleane gone off the earth in thirteene weeks. Some of the snow remained at Mindipe till midsummer . . . people did die so fast that it was the greatest parte of their work (which was appointed to doe that worke) to burie the dead; it being a day's work for two men, or two days work for one man, to make a grave.

There was always the danger of a quick thaw, and when it came late in January one of the victims was the celebrated 'Doll, the Pippin-woman' who sold apples on the ice.

The first recorded freezing of the Thames in London was in AD 695. In 827 it was frozen for nine weeks; in 923 for thirteen weeks; in 1061 for seven. 1086 was a wicked winter; the population was forced to warm their houses by open fires, with the result that most of the cities and towns were destroyed by fire, London included. 1234 and 1282 were especially frosty;

1410 was 'the most sharpest winter that ever man sawe'.*

In 1506 teams of horses crossed the river with impunity, and in 1564 Elizabeth 1 stepped onto the frozen Thames, which thawed and flooded disastrously on 3 January 1565. There was a frost fair in 1608 and regularly thereafter. Traditions were established. Watermen would use horses to pull boats backwards and forwards across the ice; ox-roastings were always popular:

> 'What you can buy for three pence on the shore
> Will cost you four pence on the Thames, or more.'

The winter of 1788–9 was exceptional; it was claimed that the ice at Blackfriars was eighteen feet thick. A wagon loaded with a ton of coal was pulled over the ice from Loughborough to Carlton House by thirteen strong men, whom Prinny generously rewarded with money and beer.

The last frost fair on the Thames was held during the winter of 1813–14.

The 1780s seemed, either coincidentally or for reasons too obscure to be unravelled, to produce the coldest winters – 1781–4 were all cold. In December 1784 the walnut tree in Gilbert White's garden at Selborne was savaged by frost. (Selborne is unlucky. In the hurricane of 1990 a magnificent yew tree in the churchyard at Selborne was uprooted.)

The 1880s were almost as cold as the 1780s. 1980, 1981 and 1982 as cold as the 1880s. 1981 saw record lows. In Preston Brockhurst, Shropshire, a low of −23° was recorded on 12 December, the lowest since 11 February, 1895, when Braemar recorded −27.2°, low enough to strip the bark off your caber. Coincidentally on 10 January 1982 Braemar managed precisely the same record low.

In 1982 Professor Hubert Lamb, meteorological guru at the University of East Anglia, noted a change in the prevailing winter winds from mild, damp westerlies to wicked northerlies

* *The Chronicles of the Grey Friars of London*

and north-easterlies from the Arctic and suggested that it might just herald the start of a new ice age. These arrive every 100,000 years and each is followed by a cycle of warmer weather lasting some 20,000 years. Less than a decade ago it was fashionable to believe, as Professor Lamb did, that the long-range forecast was frosty. A decade, as we now know, is a long time in meteorology.

Besides the bitter Eighties the coldest official months in the UK have been February 1895 (with a mean temperature of −1.6° at Kew and 1.7° at Manchester) followed by February 1947 (−0.9° at Kew and −1.4° at Manchester). Since 1795 there have been twenty months with a mean minus Centigrade temperature, four Decembers, ten Januarys, and six Februarys. The coldest London night of −15° was in December 1739, but the record can never be substantiated. The next coldest, 29 January 1947, fell to −9°.

All in all, 1963 was the coldest winter this century, 1684 the coldest ever, closely followed by 1740.

To put our British temperatures into some sort of context the coldest temperature ever officially recorded appears to be −89.2° in Vostok, Antarctica, where the mean annual temperature is −57.8°. I find it useful when dealing with these fearfully low temperatures to remember that −40° is the same in both Centigrade and Fahrenheit.

For low temperatures in Britain certain conditions need to be fulfilled – clear skies and inconsiderable winds, long nights and a sprinkling of fresh snow to prevent the heat escaping from the ground. The higher the site, the less atmosphere there will be above it and the greater the potential for record-breaking lows, but there are few meteorological recording stations on snow-covered plateaux, and it is probable that British temperatures often fall a good deal below what the statistics suggest.

The wind-chill factor is a recent and unwelcome innovation to the extent that until the forecasters began to refer to it, I'm convinced most of us never suffered from it. My proof? I never suffered from hay fever until the papers began including the pollen count! But wind-chill is taken seriously by the Americans. If you are transferred to one of the US bases in Antarctica you will be given the survival factor of '30 – 30 – 30'. Interpreted this means that at −30° F in a wind blowing at 30 mph your flesh will freeze in thirty seconds. If you have been brought up with Centigrade and knots you may well be a block of ice before you can translate the formula. But a rough guide used at the Met Office is that, if the temperature is freezing and the wind is 10, 20 or 30 mph, the equivalent for all normal human purposes will be −4, −10 and −14° c respectively.

Should you be unlucky enough to be on a mountainside in these sort of conditions and a St Bernard approaches you with a brandy flask, slap it sharply on the nose and send it away. Alcohol will give you a brief respite from the cold by pushing blood to the surface of the skin. You will experience a pleasant glow, but your heat loss will accelerate with a higher risk of hypothermia. Chocolates and sweets, though convenient to carry on a mountain hike, are less useful than a thermos of hot soup or a thick ham sandwich. The Scots got the matter of diet in a cold climate right, as so much else. They survived on porridge, oatcakes and cockaleekie soup against the worst the English could throw at them. The old folks at home in bitter weather should be encouraged to eat stews and soups with granary bread and jacket potatoes.

There is only one patch of permanent snow in the British Isles and that is to be found in the Cairngorms in a deep corrie on the slopes of Ben MacDhui. Even that is not truly permanent, and has completely disappeared on two occasions this century, happily to reappear with the next winter's snowfall. Ben Nevis is notable also for the coldest July temperature, −3.3° in 1888.

Snow is not unknown in mid-summer, even at low levels. On 2 June 1975 snow stopped play in cricket matches at Bradford and Buxton (not a ball bowled) and at Colchester (start delayed).

Blizzards in the British Isles are nothing to write home about (in which connection postmen have a hard-earned reputation for delivering the mail in the most desperate conditions). There was a blizzard in January 1881 that continued without interruption for three days, leaving Oxford Street buried under fifteen-foot drifts. Christmas Day, 1836, was one of the rare white Christmases (only seven in London during the present century), but a disaster for the poor people of Lewes, East Sussex. Snow had been piling up on a ridge overlooking the town for several days, and overhanging a row of cottages called Boulder Row in South Street. On the morning of the twenty-seventh the mass was dislodged and an avalanche hit Boulder Row. An eyewitness, Mrs Sherlock, described what happened: 'My daughter-in-law and I were sitting by the fire at about a quarter past ten dressing and washing the children, when Mrs Potter came in and told us to be quick and dress the baby for we must go – they expected the snow to fall on the houses every moment. She had been gone about a minute or two when it came over at once pitch dark. We were all flung down. I fell close to the bed, and I could feel part of the bedstead come over me. My daughter-in-law, I think, fell with her head against the chest of drawers. She moaned very much. After some time the baby moved and cried. I pushed it on to her, and said: "Jane, try and give the baby the breast." She said: "I've done that for the last time, mother." After that, I heard the noise of people overhead; I slipped my hand along and took hold of hers, and told her to keep her spirits up for I heard the noise of spades above, and I was sure they would dig us out. She made no answer, but only screamed, then she was dead. I then laid as still as I could till we were dug out.'

There were eight fatalities, from a gentleman of eighty-two to a girl of eleven. A tablet in the church commemorates the tragedy, and there is a pub in the town called the Snowdrop.

In 1891 the snowfall in the south-west of England was exceptional with an average of two feet over Devon and Cornwall. On 9 March the three o'clock from Paddington reached Plymouth at half past eight on the evening of the thirteenth, having spent four days in a massive drift.

There was a notable blizzard in the north Pennines in 1916. It raged for most of March. Nobody knows how much snow fell; educated guesses suggested ten feet. In February 1929, in windless conditions, a freak snowstorm on the edge of Dartmoor dumped six feet of snow on the village of Holme Chase. Residents said it was as if the snow was being 'shovelled' down.

Or consider the cold snap which wreaked such havoc in Britain – especially the usually protected south-east – during February 1991. The Home Counties enjoyed a seasonal snowfall of around six inches. As a result one-third of British Rail rolling stock was confined to the stockyards, and commuters faced delays of two hours and more. The red-faced British Rail spokesman offered several explanations – 'The sliding doors were frozen shut.' 'The electrical systems were short-circuiting.' 'The snow was the wrong sort of snow.' This last explanation delighted all who heard it and led to questions in the House of Commons. The suggestion that some sort of conspiracy had been at work to produce a new kind of snow with the sole intention of embarrassing the easily-embarrassed spokesman plumbed new depths of absurdity. Meanwhile gritting lorries were noticeable by their absence. The predictable response was that London can expect such a snowfall only once a generation and that it would be bad housekeeping to spend substantial sums of money on salting and gritting. One of the more engaging stories to come out of the winter was the tale of the manager of a London gritting depot who struggled to work only to find that he was unable to do his job because the roads were littered with the abandoned cars of people trying to get to work.*

I checked the statistics for London snow in February, and can report that between 1841 and 1949 there was some snow eight years out of ten on average, and that there was February snow every year between 1915 and 1938. During two years, 1879 and 1947, snow fell on nineteen days out of twenty-eight. The last big freeze – excluding February 1991, which was not *that* big –

* In the autumn of the same year British Rail apologised for the late arrival of trains in the Southeast with the excuse: 'Leaves on the line'.

took place in 1962–3. It started snowing at the end of December and continued until early March. Between 14 and 26 January it remained below freezing throughout the south of England, and you could walk across the Thames at Kingston; downstream the effluent from the power stations kept the water too warm.

Incidentally if you wish to bet on a White Christmas, there have been eight years this century during which recordable snow fell on the roof of the London Weather Centre; 1916, 1927, 1938, 1956, 1964, 1968, 1970 and 1976. So the proper odds should be ninety divided by eight, or better than eleven to one. More imaginatively you may have noticed that White Christmases occur most frequently in Leap Years (five out of the eight this century). So a bet in 1992 seems like a far better bet than in 1993, 1994 or 1995!

In normal winters the south of England suffers only occasionally from heavy falls of snow. The Forties were unusually snowy but between 1946 and 1975 there were only five mornings at Kew with snow cover of four inches or more, and never was there more than eight inches. February is the snowiest month, followed by January, March, December, April and November.

I love the snow. I love the way it covers and cleanses. Before it snows, I long for it to snow; when it snows, I long for it to continue; when it stops I long for it to start again. It liberates and encourages me. It gives me back a touch of youth.

10

Pink Frogs and Lights
which Dance

'Last night I saw St Elmo's stars,
With their glittering lanterns all at play.
On the tips of masts and the tips of spars,
And I knew we should have foul weather today.'

Henry Wadsworth Longfellow, *Golden Legend*

✳

'I often say, if you have a month without weather records
being broken, that's a record itself.'

John Houghton, Director of the Meteorological Office

Crop Circles

For those who have been asleep, or on another planet, for the
last few years, I should explain what crop circles are. They are
patterns of beaten-down crops found in fields of wheat or oats in
usually circular and sometimes elaborate patterns. They have
also been observed in soft snow and in the dust in the Tokyo
underground railway system. They have spawned a splendidly
eccentric new industry involving reluctant farmers whose fields
are trampled by hordes of circle-spotters, the circle-hoaxers
themselves, airborne photographers, mad-eyed scientists, and,
of course, media hounds, amongst which category I should in all
fairness count myself.

In this book of limited ambitions I shall deal only with crop
circles in Britain. Known for centuries as Devil Rings they were
thought to be associated with the Black Arts. Satan himself, or

his minions, had been out, it was said, doing a bit of nocturnal ploughing.

The circles can range from a diameter of just a few feet to more than two hundred. At least 2,000 circles have been examined and close to 1,000 have been documented. Three quarters of them occur within a mile or so and downwind of a steep hillside. They appear at night, almost instantaneously, it seems, and the only eye-witnesses are suspect. More than 50 per cent of crop circles are found in Wiltshire. In 1990 150 appeared in and around the village of Beckhampton.

Until 1986 most were simple circles, but thereafter sophistications began to appear. There were multiple circles, rings – *annulus* – around the circles, and quadrants within the circles. Rectangular shapes made a brief appearance in May 1990 at Cheeseford Head, near Winchester. Latterly there have been complex and beautiful patterns, known as pictograms.

The crop circles are identified scientifically as CEPs (Circles Effect Phenomena), but in the early days orthodox scientists would have little to do with the things. The only scientist who would was Dr Terence Meaden, a Wiltshireman, a meteorologist by training and founder and director of Meaden Coachworks. As a meteorological consultant, Dr Meaden runs the Tornado and Storm Research Organization, illogically known as TORRO. His original explanation of the circles was that they must have been produced by 'dust devils' or fair weather whirlwinds. Mr Reginald Till – I know the names are improbable but so is the subject we are dealing with – anticipated probable objections when he wrote a learned letter to the *Guardian* explaining why this theory could be consistent with the sharp-edged patterns of the crop circles.

The Met Office remained unpersuaded, being cynical about whirlwinds which remained static long enough to produce pretty patterns in the corn.

Other less scientific theories suggested that CEPs might be caused by helicopters flying upside down, by rutting deer, by fungi or vast hordes of rotating hedgehogs.

In the summer of 1990 a conference was held at Oxford Polytechnic at which 'more than 150 of the world's best scientific brains' – I quote the phrase from a respectable newspaper without comment – met to thrash out an acceptable theory. Dr Meaden amazed the delegates with a new and impressive phrase, 'plasma vortex', to describe a new and impressive type of dust devil which sucks up debris as it passes over the brow of a hill and spins it around so fast that it becomes electrically charged, glows, hums, and takes beautiful bites out of wheat and corn fields. Japanese scientists from Washida University nodded vigorously in approval, but it was hard to see how such a theory could apply to the patterns discovered in the Tokyo underground railway system.

The dust devil theory was blown sky high when the patterns began to elaborate. Dr Meaden and Japanese scholars from Washida University wondered whether sun spots could be pertinent to the increasingly complex CEPs.

It is a puzzling and fascinating phenomenon. If one were to believe in UFOs or flying saucers, the crop circles make perfect sense. The bull's-eye patterns seem entirely consistent with the down draught of a powerful retro-rocket, the four smaller circles with landing pads. The humming and glowing which have been reported by an unreliable batch of witnesses are the very stuff of UFOlogy. But what do our alien visitors *do* after they land? Merely take off again without even sampling the local brew, it seems, clearly unimpressed with the landscape, the facilities, the lack of a welcoming committee, or all of these.

If intelligent aliens (though I cannot imagine why it should be thought intelligent to spend your time making patterns in cornfields) are responsible, it would also explain the increasing elaboration of the patterns, and the intriguing pictograms. Natural scientists are at a loss to explain physical phenomena which change and develop so quickly. Nor are they happy with the recent proliferation of crop circles. Why have they been so little in evidence until the last ten years?

UFOlogists see in the pictograms clear evidence of an attempt by intelligent aliens to communicate with us. Indeed intelligent NASA scientists painted not entirely dissimilar diagrams on the sides of rocket ships sent into space. For myself I am impressed with the aesthetic dedication of hoaxers – if hoaxers they are – able secretly and silently to create such timeless masterpieces of design.

If only there were some persuasive eye-witnesses! One might have thought that if 2,000 flying saucers were to land on a small and heavily populated part of southern England, somebody somewhere would have taken a few snap-shots at the very least. On 25 August 1991, the *Mail on Sunday* produced a pair of eye-witnesses, Gary and Vivienne Tomlinson, who were photographed with a proprietary looking Dr Meaden in front of a couple of crop circles. This is what Vivienne had to say:

'We were standing on a narrow footpath at the edge of a cornfield when we saw the corn on our right was moving. There was a mist hovering above and we heard a high-pitched sound. Then we felt a strong wind pushing us from the side and above. It was forcing down on our heads so that we could hardly stay upright yet my husband's hair was standing on end, it was incredible. Then the whirling air seemed to branch into two and zig-zagged off into the distance. We could still see it like a light mist or a fog, shimmering as it moved. As it disappeared we were left standing in the circle with the corn flattened all around us. Everything became very still again and we were left with a tingly feeling. It all happened so quickly it seemed like a split second.'

Dr Meaden commented in strangely defensive phrases: 'The Tomlinsons' story is magnificent. There is no way they could have made it up.' To me it sounded almost too good to be true.

By now Dr Meaden was not a solitary voice crying in the wilderness. He had been joined by Michael Green of English Heritage and Ralph Noyes, recently retired from the Ministry of Defence, who together had formed the Centre for Crop Circle Studies.

The publicity brought money to the farmers and numerous

hoaxers appeared. Two local jokers were filmed walking round in circles with planks fitted to their feet. A group of physics students from Southampton University called themselves the Wessex Sceptics and accepted the challenge to create a crop circle and have it verified as genuine. In this they were successful. Their circle was discovered a few days later, and Dr Meaden examined it and announced that it was a splendid example of a classic crop circle and just had to be genuine. He looked bewildered rather than angry when it was pointed out that he had been duped. He proposed that while his lovely original crop circles were certainly genuine and caused by plasma vortices, it was increasingly probable that all these new-fangled sightings were hoaxes.

Others were also disappointed. Dowsers reported finding powerful energy fields within the CEPs, and the circle artificially created by the Wessex Sceptics was no exception. If dowsers had been made to look foolish over this evident fake, it cast aspersions on the whole of their noble profession.

So there for the moment the matter rests. At times I am tempted to side with the rutting deer or the rampaging hedgehogs rather than plasma vortices or pictographic aliens. Two points need to be emphasized, however. The crop circles are not dissimilar in their patterns to ley lines and standing stones, and inhabit a part of Britain rich in these mysterious and beautiful prehistoric cultures. And if nature can produce something as elaborately perfect as a snowflake – for no two snowflakes have ever been shown to be identical – without even the cooperation of 150 of the world's best scientific brains, should we not merely take the crop circles on trust and marvel at them?

Hail

Amongst the Plagues of Egypt which the Lord visited upon Pharaoh, as stubborn and disastrous a leader as Saddam Hussein, whom he much resembles, was the Plague of Hail.

And Moses stretched forth his rod toward heaven and the Lord sent thunder and hail, and the fire ran along the ground; and the Lord rained hail upon the land of Egypt. So there was hail, and fire mingled with the hail, very grievous, such as there was none like it in all the land of Egypt since it became a nation. And the hail smote throughout all the land of Egypt all that was in the field, both man and beast; and the hail smote every herb of the field, and brake every tree of the field. Only in the land of Goshen, where the children of Israel were, was there no hail.

Hail has always been a potent threat. In primitive societies arrows would be fired into thunderclouds to frighten away the evil spirits who lived there. In arguably more primitive societies today rockets are fired into thunderclouds to disperse the hailstones.

In May 1926 hailstones as big as baseballs fell onto Dallas, but the 1950 tornado which devastated southern and eastern England in May 1950 dropped hailstones of more than six inches in diameter onto Ascott House near Linslade and North Crawley, Bucks. I remember those storms well, and watched with amazement as children in Arundel High Street threw snowballs made from the soft hail which lay several inches deep on every side. Generally accepted as the world record hailstones were the ones which landed in and around Coffeyville, Kansas, in September 1970 and weighing in at 750 grams (about 27 ounces).

Even these pale into insignificance compared with ice-bombs. One landed on the Burton Road, Manchester, on 2 April 1973 at the surprised feet of Dr Griffiths, who just happened to be not only a postgraduate from the University but also an official 'lightning watcher' for the Electrical Research Organization. The largest part of the 'bomb' to survive the impact weighed twenty-two ounces, and Dr Griffiths estimated that the original missile was two-thirds as heavy. He subjected the ice-bomb to numerous tests, concluding that it was certainly composed of cloud water (not the discharge from the toilet of a passing aircraft – a frequent explanation for such phenomena). There have been numerous reports of ice-bombs going back centuries. Some are clear, some layered, vast, and an aggregation of smaller hailstones. One in November 1950 sliced through the neck of a sheep grazing peacefully in North Molton, Devon.

Even weirder was the turtle coated in ice which plummeted onto Vicksburg, Ohio, and the five German pilots who bailed out of their doomed plane over the Alps in 1930 and were coated with ice in a vicious thundercloud, eventually falling to earth several minutes later as human hail. One survived.

Unusual Rain

The American State Department has been blamed for a good many crimes, and is seldom guiltless. But it was *not* guilty as charged over the yellow rain that fell over Laos, Kampuchea, and Afghanistan during 1981. It was not some sinister new defoliant or nerve gas. The criminals were the honeybees (Apis Dorsala) which dropped their faeces *en masse* during an evacuation – or could I have phrased that more tactfully?

Yellow rain in Britain is not uncommon. In August and October 1987, large amounts of sand suspended within rain clouds were deposited over much of England from Liverpool to the Isle of Wight to the delight of car-wash proprietors. The Met Office denied that the sand came from the Costa Brava:

'The Spanish wouldn't get the sort of temperatures you need to get the sand into the air. We're fairly certain this came from the Sahara, sucked up by warm air currents and carried here by high level winds.'

Two years earlier sandstorms in Algeria had resulted in a substantial sprinkling of Saharan sand, without rain, over much of Britain. In the French Alps they point with pride to yellow snow on the lower slopes of Mont Blanc. And in the Swiss Alps blood-coloured rain and snow have fallen in and above Locarno; that too was thought to have been caused by Saharan sand.

Frogs fell over Trowbridge, Wilts, in 1939, and dust devils were thought to be responsible. It is not that uncommon for frogs to rain down, but the frogs which fell onto Stroud, Gloucestershire, in October 1987 were decidedly unusual, being pink. Startled scientists suggested that the frogs could be a rare albino strain sucked up over Africa and Spain.

Fish resolutely refuse to stay where they belong, in rivers and seas. Dr Robert Conny wrote to his friend, Dr Robert Plot, in 1686, about a shower of fishes in a thunderstorm; they fell into a field at Cranstead near Wrotham in Kent:

'The Fishes were about the Length of a Man's Little Finger, and judged by all that saw them to be young whitings, many of them were taken up and showed to several Persons . . . The Quantity of them was estimated to be about a Bushel, being all together.'

Minnows and sticklebacks fell profusely over Mountain Ash, Glamorganshire, in 1859. According to the *Cardiff and Merthyr Guardian* there were several thousand of them. Worcester was deluged with 'periwinkles' in 1881. These winkles, as we now refer to them, were live and much sought after by prospectors, one man apparently collecting two pecks.

'In one large shell, which a boy picked up in the lane and gave to Mr Joseph Phillips, of St John's, was a living hermit crab.'

Less fortunate were the inhabitants of Hendon, near Sunderland, in August 1918. Several hundred sand eels rained down on them, but all were found, not only to be dead but stiff enough to break as they struck the ground. Other reports identify crabs and dabs, smelts and starfish. The phenomenon is not confined to Britain, but even stranger stories are reported from further afield.

A treasure chest having been whirled into the air in Gorky in 1940, it apparently rained silver coins. And in New Orleans, where cemeteries are often built above ground, it rained skulls, skeletons and coffins after storms battered down an old wall confining a catacomb of a thousand sealed vaults.

Waterspouts

The cause of most of these eccentric precipitations is water-spouts. Sea-weed, driftwood, spars from old boats, and marine flotsam and jetsam are sucked up and spat out by these awe-inspiring and unusual events.

In 1233 Roger of Wendover described seeing off the south coast of England: 'two huge snakes fiercely battling in the air . . . After a long struggle one overcame the other and drove it into the depths.' This is how David Porter, an Isle of Wight teacher, described a waterspout which he observed and photographed on 7 August 1987.

'It began at about 1.10 and lasted for no more than four minutes. A grey funnel appeared from the base of thick, low cloud at the north end of Yarmouth Pier. The funnel expanded at the base and the top into a solid, grey, rotating column. A cloud of spray fifty feet high and thirty feet broad developed around the base of the funnel. The base could not travel as fast as the rest and a kink developed in the middle. Eventually the funnel was so thick that the mass of water within it could not be sustained; the funnel narrowed in the middle and collapsed with an obvious heavy mass of water returning to the sea. The top of the funnel disappeared into the cloud.'

This waterspout which another observer tellingly described as 'silent but powerful', was not a huge one; some British spouts have been known to extend more than a mile high. They are of course the marine equivalents of 'twisters' or 'dust devils', one of which I gleefully snapped as it advanced with silent menace across the plains of Kansas and Nebraska.

Mr Kenyon from Winchester actually sailed through one in August 1974. He noted that the water rose anti-clockwise into a column which was a muddy green-brown at the base. The waterspout was accompanied by a violent electrical storm with bolts of forked lightning 'appearing to be a yard or more in width'.

There is great variety in Waterspouts. They can rise to anything from a few hundred to a few thousand metres. They can crawl along at a slow walking pace, or race along at the speed of a fast car. They appear singly and in groups, by day or by night, in calm or in stormy conditions.

Moonbows

The moon needs to be particularly bright, and it needs to be rising or setting as the rain falls. The rain should be quite violent, which it seldom is at dusk; consequently moonbows are rare occurrences. Anaximenes (c. 546 BC) writes about them, but Aristotle confessed that he had only heard of two examples in half a century.

Colours are not observable in moonbows, merely shades of grey, because the source of the light is insufficiently intense to stimulate the colour sensitive cells of the retina. I have never heard or read of a double moonbow. But my heart leaps up when I behold a double rainbow in the sky. Intriguingly in the ghostly second bow, the colours are reversed from those of its brighter sibling.

Parhelia, or Inverted Rainbows

I quote from Charles Ashley Canes Wilson, Professor of Electrical Engineering at McGill University, who wrote in *The Times* in 1882 about a phenomenon he had observed in Bucharest: 'This . . . magnificent phenomenon called the parhelia is caused by the sun shining through an atmosphere filled with minute crystals of ice. The sun is surrounded by two rings and flanked on each side by two cross-shaped masses of golden light.

'Above the inner ring is an inverted arc, crystal white, and above the outer ring another inverted arc brilliantly coloured like a rainbow. The whole is seldom seen in this country, but parts of it may sometimes be seen. Some years ago I saw it completely in Canada, and was able to identify it with the vision of Ezekiel, who gives a very accurate description of the whole phenomenon.'

A correspondent to *The Times* in 1941 reported a small inverted rainbow to the north-west of Wentworth.

St Elmo's Fire

Also known as St Nicholas Fire, Corpo Santo, or Corpo Sant. Caesar's legionaries watching electrical discharges dart from the tips of their pikes and crackle around their swords, took the sign as a favourable augury. The Greeks called a single glow Helena, and a double discharge Castor and Pollux.

St Elmo was an Italian bishop martyred in AD 304. The sailors on Columbus's second voyage, indeed most sailors on most voyages, have been encouraged by the Fire: 'When that blessed light was about to leave us . . . we called for mercy. And when we thought we were dead men, the sea suddenly grew calm.'

There is a reason why St Elmo's Fire is considered a sign of better things to come, because it is only seen after the eye of the storm has passed. This seems to suggest that Henry Longfellow was no meteorologist (see the quotation at the top of this chapter).

On 25 June 1888, Edward, Prince of Wales, stood on the gallery of the tower at the summit of the Puy-de-Dome. When he took off his hat, his hair stood on end. Lifting his arms above his head, there was a crackle of electricity from his fingertips. When he pointed his walking stick to the sky, electricity danced at the end of it.

The Aurora Borealis

'I went on deck this evening in a rather gloomy frame of mind, but was nailed to the spot the moment I got outside. There is the supernatural for you – the northern lights flashing in matchless power and beauty over the sky in all the colours of the rainbow! Seldom or never have I seen the colours so brilliant. The prevailing one at first was yellow, but that gradually flickered over to green, and then a sparkling ruby-red began to show at the bottom of the rays on the under-side of the arch. And now from the far-away western horizon a fiery serpent writhed itself up over the sky, shining brighter and brighter as it came. It split into three, all brilliantly glittering. Then the colours changed. The serpent to the south turned almost ruby-red, with spots of yellow; the one in the middle yellow, and the one to the north, greenish white. Sheaves of rays swept along the side of the serpents, driven through the ether-like waves before a storm wind. They swayed backward and forward, now strong, now fainter again. The serpents reached and passed the zenith. Though I was thinly dressed and shivering with cold, I could not tear myself away till the spectacle was over, and only a faintly glowing fiery serpent near the eastern horizon showed where it had begun. When I came on deck later the masses of light had passed northward and spread themselves in incomplete arches over the northern sky. If one wants to read mystic meanings into the phenomena of nature, here, surely, is the opportunity.'

Thus Fridtjof Nansen, the Norwegian explorer, striving to describe in words a phenomenon that has mystified, inspired and maddened observers down the centuries. Photographers have also been defeated by the efflorescence, luminescence, and grandeur of the aurora. Lithographs by Harald Moltke (1871–1960) and more recently photographs by Torbjorn Lovgren* come close, but the pictures in Bill Forsyth's fine film, *Local Hero*, in which Peter Riegert in a red phone box on the western coast

---

* *Aurora* by Harald Falck-Ytter (Floris Books, Anthroposophic Press, Edinburgh, 1985) contains both lithographs and photographs, and gives a fair impression of the indescribable.

of Scotland describes the northern lights to Burt Lancaster on an interrupted telephone line to Texas fall far short of the full effect.

Most Eskimo and Indian tribes have mythological stories about the origins of the lights. One Canadian Indian explains, 'When I was a boy, people respected the northern lights as messengers of our spirits. People also said that some men and women can bring the northern lights down and make them obey their commands. You only have to walk outside, rub your hands together and whistle, then the northern lights will come down and sing and dance for you. When I was a young man I tried it once and it worked.'

But what causes the phenomenon? According to Christopher Hansteen (1784–1873), the aurora is directly related to fluctuating magnetic fields. We now know that the ionosphere is an excellent electrical conductor, and luminous gases in the ionosphere become electrically charged to produce the startling effects. The aurora is not in any way a reflection of the sun.

The auroral zone runs through northern Norway (Tromso), northern Canada (Hudson Bay), northern Alaska, and the vast northern reaches of the Russian continent. Here the display is visible almost every night. Even in the Shetlands you can expect to see it on a hundred nights a year; at its richest in summer, and as far as possible from brightly lit conurbations. The further south the greater the cloud cover and haze and the less frequent the sightings, but there is nowhere on earth that the aurora can never be seen – just once every ten years or so in Mexico and Japan.

Equally awe-inspiring, though seen by fewer people, is the Aurora Australis, seen over the icy southern wastelands. Captain Scott, who described it beautifully in his diary notes, published posthumously, was deeply moved by what he saw:

'One wonders why history does not tell us of "aurora" worshippers, so easily could the phenomenon be considered the manifestation of "god" or "demon". To the little silent group which stood at gaze before such enchantment it seemed profane to return to the mental and physical atmosphere of our house.'

. . . .

11

Everything Under Control

'The rain it raineth every day
Upon the just and unjust fella
But more upon the just because
The unjust hath the just's umbrella.'
Traditional

When Saddam Hussein gave the order for the Kuwaiti oil wells to be set alight he was breaking a United Nations Convention signed in 1977 by thirty-three countries, although not by China or France. I doubt whether the knowledge would have deterred him.

The idea of changing the climate as a weapon against your enemies is as old as some of the hills. Attempting to make rain, the Prophets of Baal danced and cut themselves with knives but still the sun shone. Elijah offered up a sacrifice to Yahweh which resulted in a downpour. Yahweh 1 Baal 0. Joshua, apparently, made the sun stand still and gained a notable success as a result. Rainmakers were as popular in peacetime as in war. Marco Polo reported that the priests of the Grand Khan were able to prevent rain falling by the power of their incantations.

American patents were granted for chemical rainmakers as long ago as 1894. Frank Melbourne, an Australian, had a successful early career as a rainmaker but failed to repeat his successes in the United States and took his life in a Denver hotel in 1894. Even more celebrated was Charles Hatfield, the 'moisture accelerator', who was immortalized by Richard Nash in a play and by Saul Bellow in a novel, both entitled *The Rainmaker*. Hatfield was hired to produce rain over a parched San Diego, and torrential rain followed at once, washing away houses and destroying a dam. Many citizens filed for damages against Hatfield, but the California Supreme Court ruled that the rain had been an Act of God, not an act of Hatfield. The City of San Diego therefore concluded that if the rain had been an Act of God it was quite unnecessary to pay Hatfield the $10,000 it had promised him. A statue has been erected to Hatfield at Lake Moreno, where the dam burst.

General Electric made a serious attempt to create rain by 'seeding' clouds in 1946. The scientists Schaeffer and Langmuir began with frozen carbon dioxide, then turned to silver iodide lead. These rain-making experiments were of great interest to the US Defence Department who employed the system as part of the war effort in Indo-China, but, despite 2,600 seeding sorties over Laos and the Plain of Jars ('Operation Popeye'), the enterprise failed to interfere with the Viet Cong supply lines and succeeded only in turning an American commando camp into a sea of mud.

It was far more effective, the military concluded, to spray herbicides on the forests, and to bulldoze the rubber plantations. A mere 47,489 canisters of silver iodide were used to seed clouds, but nineteen million gallons of defoliants were sprayed over South Vietnam and 6,727,084 tons of bombs were dropped, many of them incendiaries. Effects on the local climate must have been cataclysmic but were unrecorded.

Attempts were apparently made in 1969 and 1970 by the CIA and the Pentagon to wreck the Cuban sugarcane harvest by ensuring that rain fell elsewhere than over Cuba. Castro had staked his reputation on a record harvest, and came close to resignation when the harvest failed.

Meanwhile the peaceable Russian Politburo, which had been toying with the idea of diverting the river which flows into the Arctic so that it flowed into the Caspian Sea, instructed its scientists to ensure that the clouds over Moscow dispersed in time for the Revolution Day Parade of 1982, encouraging the precipitation to fall on less privileged comrades elsewhere. On top of the Lenin Mausoleum the sun was so bright that President

Brezhnev was observed to be wearing tinted glasses. The Russians also claimed to have had great success in protecting their arable land from hailstorms by firing radar-controlled guns and missiles into the clouds in which the hailstones were forming, a technique used to good effect in and around Peking.

Weather manipulation or climate control, as it is more tactfully known, is eminently feasible but expensive and controversial. Israel has been inducing rainfall artificially for some years, not so much making it rain when it has no wish to, but encouraging it to rain more heavily by sprinkling silver iodide filings on the clouds. The trouble with cloud seeding, whichever chemicals are involved, is that rain clouds can be encouraged to drop their load, but can only be created when meteorological conditions are favourable.

Neighbouring Arab countries have not always been as grateful as they might have been for Israel's enterprise. If it rains over Israel it is less likely to be raining elsewhere.

In 1977 Washington State legislature passed an emergency programme to seed the clouds over the Cascades at a cost of $125,000. Idaho was not too pleased, and insisted that rain should not be induced to fall over Washington rather than its own parched prairies. The lawyers had a good time; there was plenty of mileage in considering who – if anybody – owned the water suspended in the atmosphere. The legal implications have never been satisfactorily resolved, and attempts to manipulate the weather have become less fashionable.

Disregarding the recalcitrance of China and France, most sensible people would agree that there is something immoral in manipulating the weather for military ends. Nor has it been particularly successful. In 1975 an official Canadian survey investigating techniques of climate control listed nineteen theoretically feasible methods, but concluded that only seven were practicable. These were dispersing cloud or fog; generating fog and cloud with chemicals; inducing violent hailstorms; generating or directing big storms; making rain or snow;

stimulating volcanoes; and burning vegetation on a large scale. The most likely military technique – the dispersal of fog or cloud over a projected target area – would only be satisfactory as a tactical weapon, if local conditions were favourable.

Despite the Canadian survey there is no question that some governments have already investigated particularly sinister aspects of climate control. Monsoon rains can be exacerbated by cloud-seeding. Subterranean faults can be lubricated by pumping in fluid under high pressure in order to set off earthquakes (though how this could be used tactically to damage an enemy is extremely obscure). Holes can be blown in the ozone layer above enemy territory to subject the inhabitants to ultra-violet radiation. Efforts might be made to melt the polar icecaps. Nuclear explosions could be generated underwater to create tidal waves. It has even been suggested that a sonic generator tuned to an infrasound frequency could induce 'feelings of depression, fear, panic, terror and despair' by interfering with the electrical impulses of the human brain.

We have been lucky. Despite rather than because of international treaties, attempts to inflict heinous damage on your enemies by interfering with the climate have been rare events and singularly unsuccessful. Even the effects of Saddam's incendiary madness have been less momentous than had been feared.

Momentous enough, however. Wildlife, and particularly birds, suffered horribly, many dying from haemolytic anaemia, brought on by ingesting oil. Mammals, such as wild foxes which preyed on the dead birds, would also die. Humans, already vulnerable to respiratory diseases such as asthma, pneumonia and pleurisy, were drastically affected. Acid rain, soot and chemicals took their toll on local vegetation. But because the pall of smoke never rose to the stratosphere (fifteen kilometres above the ground), the effects remained local. It was a dreadful warning of what the consequences could be of a total environmental war. But it was contained. And the volcanic eruption of Mount Pinatubo in June 1991 was far more momentous in its effects on the climate. That one eruption is expected to lower temperatures by half a celsius degree, cancelling a century of man-made global warming.

If only one had the know-how to use these forces for good! If only one could redirect a powerful hurricane away from centres of population! Unfortunately the forces unleashed in a tropical storm are too vast to be controlled with the technology currently available. It will be many years before they can be.

Space scientists working on the colonization of Mars and other planets are investigating creating what they call a 'World House'. They ambitiously plan to stretch a roof some two kilometres high above the surface of 85 per cent of Mars. Under the roof earthlings would live in an artificial atmosphere with all – or almost all – the climatic conditions we associate with life on earth. It is not planned to fly these New Martians by rocketship from earth, because millions of people could never be transported in this way without disastrously polluting our own atmosphere. These 'brave new world' citizens would be artificially conceived with great care in test tubes lest hereditary diseases afflicted them. A handsome, healthy race of greenhouse dwellers would enjoy Martian weather just as we enjoy ours. Why does the prospect fill me with dread?

12

. . . .

Security Blanket or Microwave?

'We are conducting a giant experiment on a global scale by increasing the concentration of trace gases in the atmosphere without knowing the environmental consequences.'

World Meteorological Organization (1985)

Look at it like this. Scientists need funding for more sophisticated toys but in a world starved of ready cash, funding is reserved for those areas considered critical, such as feeding the starving and curing AIDS.

The scientists put their shaggy heads together. 'If only,' they conclude, '*we* had a crisis.' And then one can imagine them all beginning to smile the same rather sinister smile.

The politicians have problems too. Once upon a time it was enough to send a gunboat or an Exocet or a Scud to win a limited war against foolishly impelled and suitably foreign-looking opposition. There were votes to be had in the Falklands Campaign, and in Grenada, and there might have been votes in the Iran Hostage affair if things had not turned out so unpalatably. Stormin' Norman finds himself with a knighthood and a political career – if he is foolish enough to desire one – and even our gentlemanly officers are promoted when the smoke clears.

But what if there are no longer any suitably popular wars at conveniently regular intervals? If one cannot kick the hell out of any over-ambitious foreigner, then one needs to find a substitute crisis. The environment? Plenty of votes in that.

'We have a crisis,' say the scientists to the politicians.

'So?' say the politicians.

'We need funds. Lots of them,' say the scientists.

'But is it *really* a crisis?' ask the politicians, eyes sparkling. 'Is it – what's the phrase? – potentially apocalyptic?'

The scientists smile another of their sinister smiles. 'Absolutely,' they aver.

Now let me quote a passage from the *Observer* (August 1989) reporting on the Fifth International Assembly of Meteorology and Atmospheric Physics:

'Last week's opening session was kicked off by the Junior Environment Minister, Mrs Virginia Bottomley, with a speech as polished and green as a Cape apple. She told the delegates proudly that Britain was to spend £10 million on research into the weather and climate change.

'It knocked the socks off the foreign delegates. "Zis is amazing," said a long-haired and sincere young Austrian studying how pollution is carried by the weather. "Never have I heard a politician speak like zis." Other foreign delegates were equally impressed.'

By November 1989 Margaret Thatcher announced at the United Nations that Britain was to set up a centre for climate prediction, and that it would concentrate on the ecological measures confronting the globe. A further £100 million would be pledged to protect and regenerate the rainforests.

Everything seemed to be going according to plan. The scientists report a crisis. The government responds to it. Both nationally and internationally hats are flung into the air. But forecasting remains a chancy business. Who would have guessed – what computer model could possibly have predicted – that within a year Margaret Thatcher would have been toppled, and replaced by the son of a circus acrobat?

You think this is an unfair simplification? I agree with you. Cynicism was supposed to have died with the last Labour Government. And I have no right to impute the worst possible motives to our hard-working scientists and our benevolent politicians. But I do have the right to examine whether the current ecological scares are soundly based, and whether the gloomy prognostications of global warming are more than just the fashionable concerns of a rudderless age drifting helplessly through the squalls of fashion and intellectual chic.

Important questions need to be asked.

Is the globe really warming? If so, why? And does it matter?

Is there really a greenhouse effect? Is this the cause of global warming? What other causes could there be?

Is there really a hole in the ozone layer? Is it reversible? If there is such a hole does it have an effect on the climate? If so, what?

I want scientists to have the shiny new toys for which they so passionately long. I have nothing against politicians, and cannot find it in me to blame them for wishing to hang on to office. But I do sympathize with the Congressman who asked Steve Scheider of the US National Centre for Atmospheric Research:

'Do you mean to say that you guys have spent a billion dollars of our money telling us that winter is cold and summer is hot?'

'Yes, sir,' Scheider answered, 'and we're very proud of that!'

So is the globe really warming?

The 'hothouse effect' was first observed and named in 1827 by Baron Joseph Fourier, a French mathematician who became insane, wrapping himself in numerous layers of clothes and falling disastrously downstairs. That was in the early nineteenth century. At the end of the century the Nobel Laureate, Svante Arrhenius, a Swedish chemist, theorized that twice the amount of carbon dioxide in the atmosphere would lead to a global temperature increase of fifty degrees Centigrade. About fifty years later and fifty years ago the notion that carbon dioxide in the atmosphere was significantly augmented by the burning of fossil fuels was propounded, but the scientific monitoring of carbon dioxide levels did not begin until 1957. Since then the average concentration has been rising with ominous regularity from 315 in 1958 to 352 in 1988.

Carbon dioxide (CO_2) constitutes about .03 per cent of the atmosphere. The bulk consists of 78 per cent nitrogen,

20 per cent oxygen. CO_2 is only dangerous in concentrations of 10 per cent or more. As a key ingredient in photosynthesis it is vital to life on earth. Now it seems to have been accumulating in the atmosphere and acting as a one-way mirror, allowing the sun's heat to pass through but absorbing the heat which is reflected back from the earth. All fires produce carbon dioxide, domestic fires, industrial chimneys, volcanic eruptions. Fossil fuels give off the most; nuclear power gives off none. Half of the carbon dioxide remains in the atmosphere, the other half seems to be soaked up by plankton on the surface of the sea or forests on land. If we were to sprinkle iron filings on the sea, and replant the trees we have been felling, we would return our atmosphere to its traditional balance.

That is what most scientists believe. But there were – and still are – doubts about the correlation of carbon dioxide in the atmosphere and global warming. In the *Geographical Magazine* for November 1978 we find D. W. Bowen, the advisory editor, writing:

'The past 10,000 years have been but a warm respite from a planetary glacial age which has lasted for several million years. Recent startling evidence suggests that the onset of glacial conditions can occur within 100 years.'

He went on to startle his readers with the recent evidence. He was by no means alone in his views. Reid Bryson at the University of Wisconsin-Madison had already spoken of a return to the Little Ice Age and blamed pollution which, he believed, blocked out the heat of the sun. George and Helena Kukla of Columbia University even speculated that we might be seeing a return to a full-scale Ice Age. Their colleague at Columbia, Wallace Broecker, was one of the first to coin the phrase 'greenhouse effect'.

Battle was joined. Sir Fred Hoyle thought the world was getting colder. Most scientists disagreed. It was also commonly believed during the Sixties and Seventies that one of the principal causes of climate changes was nuclear testing which released large quantities of nitrogen oxides into the atmosphere with significant effects on the ozone layer.

The long hot summer in Britain of 1989, the extreme heatwave in August 1990, and the endlessly sunny late summer of 1991, led many who should have known better to conclude that we were already in the sweaty throes of a sinister greenhouse monster. But the summers of 1989, 1990 and 1991, like the storms of 1987 and 1990, are *weather*, not climate. If we look at British records it may set recent events in context. The warmest months have been:

January	1916
February	1779
March	1957
April	1865
May	1833
June	1989
July	1983
August	1975
September	1729
October	1969
November	1818
December	1934

Overall the hottest recorded year was indeed 1989. But not by much.

How are these records established? They come from an average of Britain's weather stations. As you might expect the preponderance of these stations are in urban communities, and the oldest maintained records going back to the 1700s emanated from the centre and south of England. So one should anticipate, as temperatures in towns increase and temperatures in country areas do not, a developing imbalance. However, we have no way of knowing how accurate were the thermometers and the other tools of the trade used by early meteorologists, because they made their own instruments. They probably were accurate as to freezing point which is not difficult to find, but may well not have been accurate higher up the scale.

A recent scholarly estimate (by Phil Jones of the Climate

Research Unit and David Parker of the Met Office) based upon worldwide records over the last 130 years suggests that there has been significant global warming since 1900. The Centigrade variations from the mean established between 1951 and 1980 are:

1860	−0.22
1870	−0.19
1880	−0.18
1890	−0.21
1900	−0.20
1910	−0.30
1920	−0.20
1930	−0.10
1940	level
1950	+0.10
1960	level
1970	+0.07
1980	−0.02
1990	+0.21

This small but noticeable warming trend over 130 years is evidence of global warming but scarcely conclusive. Indeed one of the latest and most influential studies on the subject put together by Roy Spenser of NASA and John Christy of the University of Alabama (*Science Magazine*, 29 March 1990) suggests otherwise. 'While future global temperature variations are not specifically addressed, the decade from 1979 through 1988 showed no net warming or cooling trend.' The reason this study reached the surprising conclusion it did was because it measured temperatures from satellites rather than at ground level, and recommended that this should be the standard way of monitoring future global temperature changes. Temperatures thus measured are more accurate, say Roy and John, because satellites reach parts other methods cannot each – oceans, deserts and wildernesses especially.

There is also the evidence of sunspot cycles. For many years it has been known that solar activity has an effect on the weather. A team of scientists at the Massachusetts Institute of

Technology, led by Nicholas Newell of Arlington, analysed temperature variations from 1856 to 1986 and discovered that they walked remarkably neatly hand in hand with solar magnetic cycles. The mathematics of it all are complex but may be found for those with burning curiosity in *Geophysical Research Letters*, Vol. 16, p. 311. Their conclusions? 'There is no appreciable difference between temperatures at the beginning and end of the record.' Ironically there have been several exceptionally hot years since 1986 which must have some marginal effect on their conclusions. All the same their researches, along with those from the Alabama team, certainly pour some cold water on the global warming theories.

What we have to remember is that some 120,000 years ago Britain was warm enough for hippopotamuses to graze and wallow in Yorkshire – 120,000 years ago the earth's orbit around the sun was more elliptical than circular, and climate patterns all over the world would have been unrecognizable to a time-traveller from 1991. These wobbles in the earth's orbit were first proposed over a century ago by an unpretentious Scot, James Croll, and his theories were developed by Milutin Milankovitch, a Serb who has given his name to these 'Milankovitch wobbles', though perhaps they should really be called 'Crolls'.

There appear to be three cycles during which the tilt of the earth's axis to the sun varies – every 21,000 years, every 41,000 years, and every 100,000 years – and the incidence of recorded Ice Ages relates directly to these wobbles. Nothing the government, or any government, could possibly do about the earth's orbit, and nothing it could possibly do about many of the other influences upon our own parochial climate, such as sunspots, volcanic eruptions, and that mystifying phenomenon known as El Nino – more about them later.

Many American cities feature a television channel devoted to weather forecasts round the clock. Satellite pictures, computer models, charts, and comical met men (like Steve Martin in *LA Story*) feed what seems to be an insatiable public and commercial appetite for instant climatic gratification. For them – perhaps for you too – 120,000 years would seem an impossibly long time, but it was just 100 years ago that London perspired under its longest ever drought. From 4 March until 13 May 1893, a total of seventy-three days, there was no measurable rainfall. If such freakish conditions repeated themselves today, one can just imagine how informed and uninformed sources would leap into print with ominous theories about global warming. (We're fortunate not to endure the climate of the Atacama Desert in Chile. There a drought of 400 years ended in 1971, but the annual rainfall remains officially 'zero'.)

Let us look back not 120,000 but 120,000,000 years, to the age of the dinosaurs. From such fossil evidence as we have it seems that the earth was ten to fifteen Centigrade degrees warmer than it is today. Turn the clock back as far as it will turn, four billion years back to when the sun was in its infancy and its rays far fainter than today. Then we know that at least some of the planet must have been above freezing point for primitive life forms to develop, and carbon dioxide levels must have been a thousand times in excess of what they are today. Eventually the sun's rays will falter and fail, and there will be no further talk then of global warming.

The problem of meteorological computer modelmakers attempting to chart the likely progression of global warming is a similar problem to that faced by short-term forecasters; there are just too much data, and no way of estimating their proportionate importance. Richard Lindzen, Professor of Meteorology at MIT, went so far as to state (December 1991): 'There is no real reason in the world to assume that any computer model of the climate is right.'

Take clouds. They are mostly air but they form when water condenses around dust particles or other minute nuclei. They reflect sunlight back to outer space. They keep the surface of the earth cool. But they also absorb infra-red rays from the earth, keeping the surface of the earth warm. Clouds in the tropics differ from clouds in the temperate zones. Clouds over water have little in common with clouds over land masses. They are our sunshades and our security blankets. According to the Goddard Institute for Space Studies in New York City, clouds amplify the greenhouse effect, but exert an overall cooling effect on the planet. But the game is still for winning because there may be another twenty or more chemical processes taking place in the clouds simultaneously.

El Nino (meaning 'The Little Boy' or 'The Christ Child') is our latest scapegoat. In a remote area of the western Pacific, 400 miles north of New Guinea, there occurs every few years an interaction between the ocean and the atmosphere which is now believed to be a hugely significant factor in determining ocean currents and therefore short-term climatic changes. The warm years of 1983, 1987, and 1988 followed the appearance of El Nino in 1982–3 and 1986–7. In 1983 especially, dust storms and heat waves in Australia, droughts in Africa and Asia, floods in Ecuador, Peru (rainfall 340 times the average in places) and the Galapagos, blizzards in New Mexico, and cyclones in French Polynesia were all put down to El Nino. 'Gentle Jesus, meek and mild . . .' Scarcely. But what is he?

The Christ Child is a warm-water current which strikes the Peruvian coast around Christmas time. It was named by South American anchovy fishermen. The waters around Peru and Ecuador are characteristically cold, forming a part of the Humboldt current which sweeps north from the southernmost tip of Chile. But when El Nino puts in an appearance the sea temperature rises by four degrees within twenty-four hours, and the effect on marine life is devastating. The water within El Nino can reach 34° Centigrade, and is considerably more saline than the sea around it. It also creates huge whirlpools.

The peculiar characteristics of El Nino were charted by the 190 scientists aboard the Royal Research Ship Charles Darwin, which circumnavigated the globe. In a delicately balanced atmosphere in which the beating of a butterfly's wing can cause a typhoon, it is obvious that so violent a change in the sea-water, and the currents which eddy from it, will have significant consequences. It has been suggested by Michael Moseley of the University of Florida that the severe coastal flooding which inundated Peru between AD 600 and 1100 and the simultaneous upland droughts were the effects of the mischievous El Nino.

Many of the ancient cultures never recovered from these disasters.

For all our satellites and technology, we still know far too little about the earth's orbit, or the chemical processes within the clouds, or what triggers El Nino and other such mysterious currents in the sea, to be able effectively to programme our computer models. And the evidence of global warming, such as it is, may be more closely related to any of these than to the acknowledged, observed and recorded hole in the ozone layer.

Further controversy has been created by the claims of Dr Bruce Denness, formerly of Newcastle University, whose studies of the ocean seabed have led him to conclude that past weather patterns are contained within submarine sediment as isotopes of oxygen. From this evidence, which seems to have accurately predicted the hot summers and mild winters of the Eighties, Denness believes that rising temperatures are due, not to the greenhouse effect, but to a natural increase in gravity which is pulling the earth nearer to the sun. He is concerned that if these symptoms are misinterpreted, we will be taking ever more drastic steps in quite the wrong direction. But there is no comfort in his research; we will be getting hotter more quickly as a result of gravitational forces, and there will be less we can do about it. No wonder his conclusions have been generally ignored by the experts.

If we accept the findings of the Met Office report and the IPCC (Inter-Governmental Panel on Climate Change), which are in significant conflict with the NASA study I referred to earlier, or Dr Denness's conclusions, we must acknowledge that global warming is taking place. The IPCC reported in the spring of 1990 that over the last century air temperatures had increased by between 0.3 and 0.6 degrees Centigrade. Sea level had increased globally by between ten and twenty centimetres. It predicted an average rise in global temperatures of 1.8°c by 2020 and around 3.5°c by 2070. By then the average global rainfall will be seven per cent higher and areas of snow cover and sea ice will be significantly diminished. The Met Office experts added an important rider to the effect that the temperature changes which have already taken place *could* be explained by natural climate variability and that it would take at least another decade for any conclusions about greenhouse warming to be unequivocal.

The panel suggested that the increase already observed in global mean temperatures would lead in the future to more hot periods and fewer cold periods. In other words if the report seems to be saying nothing more than: if it's true that the world is really getting hotter, then it will probably go on getting hotter.

Global warming means enhanced levels of carbon dioxide in the atmosphere. This 'may increase productivity and efficiency of water use of vegetation. The effect of warming on biological processors, although poorly understood, may increase the atmospheric concentrations of natural greenhouse gases.' These natural greenhouse gases are principally water vapour and carbon dioxide.

The report ended with an admission – scarcely necessary in the context of what had preceded it – that the panel did not fully understand 'the various climate-related processes, particularly those associated with clouds, oceans, and the carbon cycle', and called for further exchange of international data and – wait for it – increased funding.

Despite the vagueness of the panel's findings and the need for such an august body to hedge its bets, despite rogue scientists still insisting that the world is getting colder not warmer, one piece of evidence brooked no argument, and that was Joe Farman's discovery of the rent in the ozone layer. The debate about the ozone layer goes beyond the scope of this book, but not insofar as it impinges upon climate change.

What was most worrying about the publication in May 1985 of Farman's incontrovertible evidence was that it had been so little anticipated. And if the scientists had not anticipated it, how could they be expected to understand it, or do anything about it? John Gribbin put the argument powerfully in *The Hole in the Sky*:

'Imagine a naive scientist watching a block of ice being heated slowly. As the temperature approached melting point he could still write in his notebook that, on the basis of what he had seen so far, he predicts no significant change in the ice block if it warms further. His prediction will be in ruins as soon as the block warms above zero degrees.'

Farman had worked as part of the British Antarctic Survey, based at Halley Bay. At first he found it hard to credit the evidence of his own research. The Americans had satellites five hundred miles up and they had produced nothing comparable. So Farman sent home for newer equipment. Then there could be no doubt. Within ten years the ozone layer above Antarctica had been depleted by 50 per cent. The important questions were: Why? and: What Will Happen Next?

Why? There were many theories. CFCs (chlorofluorocarbons), invented in 1930, had become hugely important to big business – notably Dupont and ICI, and you can't get much bigger than that – and, as aerosol propellants, coolant fluids, and plastic foam, had saved a lot of people a lot of money. Unfortunately these industrial chemicals have the nasty habit of floating into the stratosphere, where ultra-violet radiation breaks them down, releasing chlorine atoms. These undergo various complex chemical changes and set about destroying the ozone. Other manufactured gases besides CFCs, which have damaging effects on our atmosphere, include methane from rotting rubbish and paddy fields, and nitrous oxide from fertilizers. Ironically ozone itself, from the chemical reaction of sunlight on exhaust fumes, is also damaging the ozone layer.

The dozen highest producers of greenhouse gas emissions are USA (20 per cent), USSR, Brazil, China, India, Japan, Germany – West Germany when the United Nations produced its league table – United Kingdom, Indonesia, France, Italy and Canada. When the figures are readjusted on a per capita basis the table reads: Canada (4.5 tonnes per person per year), Ivory Coast, Brazil, USA, Australia, East Germany, Saudi Arabia, Netherlands, United Kingdom, West Germany, USSR, and Colombia. As the population of the world increases with a further three billion to eight billion by AD 2030, any improvement as a result of national or international action is likely to be negligible. Ironically if global warming does increase severely as a result of greenhouse gas emissions, Canada, whose citizens are so profligate with their CFCs, will be the country to benefit most dramatically from the changes. The snows will melt; much of Canada could become a paradisal corn-belt. New Zealand anticipates a cornucopia of citrus and kiwi fruits. Siberia will be another beneficiary. But, if one believes the computer models, the monsoon rains will intensify and low-lying areas of southeast Asia and the sub-continent will be inundated, while much of Western Australia will be parched. There is plenty of speculation about the effect on flora and fauna throughout the world, much of it cataclysmic in its implications. Since it is more difficult and less newsworthy to predict beneficial effects of these climatic changes, few naturalists have yet done so.

Even worse, the situation monitored by Joe Farman and Jim Anderson, his American colleague from Harvard, is rapidly deteriorating, and cannot easily be reversed because the CFCs already in the atmosphere will have a deleterious effect for many years to come. What will happen if the ozone level is permanently destroyed? Ultra-violet radiation from the sun will be allowed to enter the atmosphere unimpeded, increasing the risk of cataracts and skin cancer. We cannot yet tell for sure whether it will significantly increase the heat on our planet; but it will certainly stop people from lying around and basking in it.

It is curious that the simplest solution to the ozone layer depletion, which was proposed in November 1987 by Leon Sadler in *Chemical and Engineering News,* and supported by the sensible Fred Pearce in his fine book *Turning Down the Heat* (The Bodley Head, 1989), has never been followed up. If we are destroying the ozone layer at such a rate, Sadler inquired, why do we not merely inject more ozone into the stratosphere? Estimating that the layer contains about three million tonnes of ozone, he computed that a replenishment of 5.4 million kilograms per day would make up the shortfall within 100 years. There are no problems about producing ozone in such quantities, or about shooting it into space. It could easily be done by commercial and military aircraft going about their regular business. It sounds too good to be true – perhaps it is – but nobody to date has cared to try it.

The effects of global warming most anticipated and most feared are the drying up of many parts of the world. But an ingenious solution to at least a part of this problem would be to adopt the procedures proposed by Newman and Fairbridge in an article in *Nature* (Vol. 320, 1986, pp. 319–21) headed: 'The Management of Sea Level Rise'. This sets out a plan for taking the water out of the sea and depositing it in natural depressions on land. Then it could be desalinated and the land irrigated.

There's a shortage of ozone in the stratosphere – put some more up there. There's a shortage of trees in the Amazonian rainforest – plant more there and elsewhere, specially bred fast-growing varieties. Parts of the planet are dying of thirst – take water to them. The simplest solutions are often the best, and not always as complicated as they might sound. (And whenever one mentions the slaughter of the Amazonian rainforests it might be appropriate to add that the Americans are cutting down forests in Oregon to supply timber to the Japanese.)

This has not been an easy chapter to write. I am no scientist, and the issues we are dealing with are hugely complex. We have scientists quarrelling with scientists and learned journals trying to have it every which way. Either the world is getting hotter or it is getting colder; some even argue that it is staying much the same. Last August I was in Devon and the temperature was as near 100 degrees Fahrenheit as dammit, and last June there was snow on the ground in the north of England. It seems to me that we are close to a situation where the only dignified thing to do is say, 'We just don't know.'

But when did experts ever up and say that? Mind you, it would be quite a story for the tabloids if they did. 'The International Congress issued a press release yesterday to admit it did not know the answers to any of the most pressing questions currently affecting our planet and its future.' It's a pleasant fantasy. But then what would happen to the funding?

how many charitable organizations, and corporate bodies, how many governments, how many of the good and the great, the captains and the kings, would dig deep into their pockets then?

The one thing we do know is what Joe Farman told us, and Farman made his discoveries on equipment that was not the most sophisticated available, and while those far better equipped than he could not see the wood for the trees, the actual situation for the computer models.

We must hope for more Joe Farmans and encourage embryonic Joes whenever we get a whiff of them, but in the meantime we must, of course, allow the scientists to continue their researches – not that they could be stopped – and hope that they will come up with incontrovertible evidence as to what is going on, because if and when they do, we shall be in a position, with our gleaming new Cray supercomputers, and our wonderful whirring space satellites, and our DOLPHINS and our DOGGIES, to deal with its worst effects. In the meantime we must do what we can where we can; stop cutting down trees, and start planting them, not just in the depleted areas of the Amazonian rainforest, but wherever erosion has been taking place. If we were to do this and to think globally rather than nationally, and to accept that things need to be done urgently rather than in a leisurely way, we might just save our planet. And even if we failed to save our planet, we could sink beneath the waves conscious at least of having done our best.

And we ought to try to keep our sense of humour. Why? Because when you read that cattle belch and fart into the air ninety million tonnes of methane a year, and that this may well contribute significantly to the destruction of the ozone layer, and when you wonder just what we can do about *that* problem, you have to smile, even as you frown.

Even as this book goes to press the Meteorological Office has revealed that temperatures are now expected to rise by only 1.5°c over the next seventy years. Sir John Houghton, the Chief Executive, suggested that some environmentalists had been guilty of scare-mongering.

13

. . . .

The Apocalypse Option

'Suicide is dangerous
It brings on many changes.'
Theme song, *Mash*

According to a report issued by an environmental group calling itself Ark just three years ago, by the year 2050 the sea will have risen eighteen feet around our coasts as a consequence of the melting of the polar ice caps. I am not too certain who Ark is (or are), but their estimate is on the gloomy side. A report produced for the Commonwealth Secretariat by a distinguished group of scientists under the chairmanship of Martin Holdgate based its recommendations on the planet warming up by between one and two degrees centigrade by the year 2030, with a 'best guess' that in such a case sea levels would rise between seventeen and twenty-six centimetres. Let us say thirty-five centimetres by 2050, fifty centimetres by 2070.

A rise of a metre would have serious but not catastrophic consequences for us, but wholly catastrophic consequences for the unfortunate inhabitants of Bangladesh, Guyana, the Maldives, Tonga, Kiribati, and Tuvalu (previously part of the Gilbert and Ellis Islands). A rise of eighteen feet would have catastrophic consequences for all of us.

Belfast is just a big puddle. Morecombe, Formby, Barrow, Fleetwood are submerged. Liverpool's docklands and water-front have gone. Wales has survived, but Port Talbot and Rhyl have vanished along with a sizeable chunk of Cardiff and Newport. Indeed the Severn Estuary now extends beyond Gloucester, has swallowed up Weston-Super-Mare and is lapping greedily at Bristol. The old-age pensioners who retired to the south coast for their health are now disconsolate – and damp. Portsmouth has quite gone, except for the top of the rusting helter skelter on the pier, along with Worthing, Eastbourne, Bognor Regis, Littlehampton and Poole. Romney Marshes are now Romney Marina, and you would need underwater sonar equipment to locate Chichester Harbour.

The east coast is a disaster area. The Essex and North Kent Marshes overlap with the Norfolk Broads as a result of which Cambridge and Peterborough are seaside towns; so is Doncaster. The Isle of Ely reverts to being an island. Does anyone still remember Hull and King's Lynn, Grimsby and Boston? Or Middlesbrough, Hartlepool, Sunderland, Berwick-on-Tweed?

London is quite submerged. All that remain really are the suburbs, a broken ring including Ealing, Wembley, Hampstead, Camden, Islington – just – and Romford to the north; Richmond Hill, Clapham, Brixton, Crystal Palace, Catford, Eltham, and Blackheath to the south. House prices in Hampstead have gone through the roof, and it has become ever so chic to live in a houseboat. It is no use trying to get to work by underground, has not been for years – never was, cynics claim – and you can row a boat over the roofs of the Houses of Parliament, attaching your painter to the minute hand of Big Ben and admiring the view of Wren spires and Sixties tower blocks. Westminster School, St Paul's and Eton College have long been evacuated; Harrow is desperately popular. There are no longer any 'dry bobs' – where would they find to pitch their wickets?

Our nuclear power stations, many of which were built on particularly low-lying land, are under water. Nobody dares to swim close enough to investigate the damage. The sight of all those mutant fish is enough to dissuade even the most fool-hardy.

It is not surprising that while we all have reason to be worried by these images of Britain in the twenty-first century, one group of business people is more worried than the rest – the insurers. It was the Insurance and Reinsurance Research Group which organized a seminar in London recently to investigate the probable effects of a rise in the sea level. Their most immediate problem was the discovery that Ordnance Survey maps start at a five-metre line. Much of Britain anyway is below the existing spring tide high water mark.

According to Dr Michael Tooley, a geographer from the University of Durham, the sea level is currently rising by a modest two millimetres a year, but Britain is noticeably tilting towards the south-east, which is behaving as though it is heavier than the north-west. The weight of guilt perhaps. Aberdeen remains the same level above the sea as it used to be, but Ipswich is subsiding by four millimetres a year. You will not be surprised to learn that, as a result of their seminar, the insurers went home to work out new ways of raising premiums on future policies, and replacing existing ones. The tilting of the country was taken seriously enough for the planning, funding and building of the Thames Barrier, an unusually enlightened case of forward planning, which has not yet been, but soon will be, properly appreciated.

If Britain, even the south-east, can live for a while with these modest changes, there are parts of the world that cannot. In 1987 the President of the Maldives, Maumoon Abdul Gayoom, inquired politely of the Commonwealth Heads of Governments whether global warming and the consequent rise of the sea level might be responsible for the exceptional flooding already suffered within his territory. The Maldives consist of 1,196 islands and few of them lie more than six feet above the surface of the sea. Within a half century it is inevitable that there will be considerably fewer than 1,196 islands left in the Maldives. The Prime Minister of Tuvalu also wrote to the United Nations inquiring to know 'for planning purposes' whether Tuvalu could look forward to a future at all, except as a warning to shipping.

The inevitable reply to such queries has to be: do not waste time and resources on trying to shore up your islands. It is not possible. Concentrate instead, in the first instance, on reducing your emissions of greenhouse gases and persuading others to do the same; your emissions are of no real consequence (America and the Russian Commonwealth countries together account for almost half the global total of carbon dioxide emissions), but by setting an example to others you may just have an outside chance of saving yourselves. While you wait you could do worse than to flood parts of your country deliberately to save other parts; and move your population to higher ground. Mount Ararat maybe.

Probably, rather than possibly, the following events are on the agenda: serious flooding in such places as Florida, Venice, New Orleans, Shanghai, Cairo and Leningrad, which still have time to defray the worst of the damage. The flooding of a sixth of Egypt's crop-growing capacity and much of Asia's paddy fields. The loss of the Maldives and Tuvalu; Bangladesh too is likely to go under. The Ebro Delta in Spain, the Rhone Delta in France, and Lac Ichkeul in Tunisia would all become unidentifiable.

But the flooding may not be the most serious effect of the warming. The earth's winds, rainfall, and ocean currents will alter. The changing balance between temperatures at the poles, which will heat up faster than tropical regions, could cause frequent and very violent storms. As we have already seen, the forecasting of future weather can be affected by the beating of a butterfly's wings in a suburban garden, so the cataclysmic effects of such fundamental changes are alarming to contemplate. But contemplate them we must.

The Department of the Environment has done a certain amount of contemplating. In 1988 it published a lively little tome, culled from the work of six groups of scientists and enticingly called: *The Possible Impacts of Climate Change on the Natural Environment in the United Kingdom.*

By the year 2050 you would sit in your deck chair under your mosquito net on a sunny summer's afternoon in Weybridge (if Weybridge is still above the water-line) and expect the temperature to be around 32°c. Your summer would be longer and drier and sunnier, though warmer and wetter in Scotland, where icebergs would menace the shipping. The birth rate in the south would fall because as the temperature increases the male's sperm count and the female's fertility decreases. Also because, as one of the scientists coyly put it: 'Intercourse is less frequent in hot weather.' (He cannot have been reading the *Sun* whose headline in 1990 ran: 'Britain has gone sex-crazy as red-hot lovers rush to do it in the great outdoors, say experts.')

We would eat less and suffer less from heart attacks, cerebrovascular, and respiratory diseases, although there could be an increase in tropical diseases. A rough estimate suggests that if the mean temperature rose by 5° the mortality rate would drop by 12.5 per cent. Scientists regard these as desiderata. My own view is that a country in which love-making is out of fashion, in which fewer babies are born and in which the old live on endlessly in sun-drenched idleness, is not entirely to be welcomed. And there are less welcome effects to be anticipated.

There would be forest fires, and insect swarms. Wheat, barley, sugar beet and potatoes would no longer grow in most of the country. In the south vineyards, sunflowers and sweetcorn would be popular options. Spruce and conifers would be replaced by trees such as sweet chestnuts, maples and limes, assuming that they were tough enough to survive the frequent hurricanes. The US, Russia and the Ukraine would lose their position as leading grain-producers to North and East Africa, China, the Middle East, and Western Australia.

Britons would become more irritable, although the loss of London's underground system should alleviate our frustration somewhat. We would suffer from food-poisoning more frequently (and snake-bites). We would have to build some hundred or so new nuclear power stations (divers will do their courageous best to regulate the toxic emanations from submerged ones) and place them on high ground, while fossil fuels would be abandoned by international agreement. The business of coastal defences would boom, but as well as massive sea-walls the designers would give us floating mats of plastic seaweed, mock rocks, and curved and honeycombed concrete breakwaters. Quite a few prophets of doom – those who could afford it – would fly off to make new homes in regulated atmospheres somewhere on Mars. But nobody would bother to take their holidays on the Costa Brava.

So what are we to do?

We might start by giving education in these matters a higher priority. At the moment the Government has decided to rationalize the teaching of science in secondary state schools by withdrawing the GCSE in Meteorology. Tremendous! The much vaunted National Curriculum has given 'the Atmosphere' a half of one of the sixteen attainment targets in science. Brilliant! And the geographers and the scientists continue to squabble over who should teach the subject. Superb!

Next we should be realistic. Chances are that the greenhouse effect is now a reality. Chances are (a 99 per cent chance, says Jim Hansen of the Goddard Institute for Space Studies, New York) that global warming is already taking place. Chances are that the depletion of the ozone layer has something to do with it. So we should seriously investigate the proposal by Leon Sadler which I detailed in the previous chapter. We should take seriously the notion of replenishing the ozone in the ozone layer by pumping more into the stratosphere.

Then we should filter nitrous oxide out of car emissions and nuclear power stations, and switch out of coal and into natural gas and *clean* nuclear energy, ensuring through the international agencies which already exist that everyone does likewise. At the same time we should be busily investigating whether the natural alternatives – wind power, wave power, solar power – are feasible on a grand scale. And we should be replanting trees in the areas suffering most critically from deforestation. If this means supping with the devil, we should bring our long spoon, and be prepared to *reward* the big operators for not cutting down the rainforests, rather than telling them politely to stop. If that fails we could ban the sale and employment of those types of wood which come from vulnerable and necessary forests.

This is urgent. Currently about 50,000 square kilometres, the size of Costa Rica, of the Amazonian Rain Forest, is cut down each year; if continuing unchecked we would have no more rainforest at all by the year 2040. What would happen then? The traditional highly humid climate, produced by water evaporating from trillions of leaves, would be replaced by long dry seasons, which would ensure that the jungle did not reseed itself. Without the jungle there would be no recycling of carbon dioxide and a serious loss of oxygen in the atmosphere. Things are already deteriorating. In the most recent Ice Age some 23,000 years ago there was 0.018 per cent of carbon dioxide in the earth's atmosphere. (These measurements are taken from bubbles in the polar ice.) By 1800 carbon dioxide made up 0.028 per cent of the earth's atmosphere; today the percentage has risen to 0.035 per cent.

It would be a help to propose a UN Resolution declaring the weather to be part of our universal heritage and make sure that the resolution has enough teeth and the scientists enough money to investigate the weather energetically and protect the environment vigorously. Some sort of international tax (1 per cent of Gross National Product) might be a starting point to argue from. If such a resolution sounds rather like pie in the sky, castles in Spain, and bats in the belfry, it is worth recalling that a similar constraint has already been applied in the case of the 1982 United Nations Convention on the Law of the Sea with respect to certain areas of the seabed ocean floor and subsoil.

'It is time that we realized that we all share a common future', announced Mr Brundtland, Prime Minister of Norway, in 1988. Statesmen like stating the obvious sententiously, but there is a serious core of truth in Mr B's platitudes. We should not be cynical until we have tried being optimistic. If international opinion can bring down *apartheid*, it should have a chance of saving our environment as well as our souls.

14

Great Men of Weather

'The simplest schoolboy is now familiar with truths for which
Archimedes would have sacrificed his life.'

Ernest Renan (1883)

In the preceding chapters I have been dealing with the extremes of British weather, and it would be courteous at least to trace a brief history of the scientists who created modern meteorology. Extraordinary men, for whom in many cases the natural world was entirely compatible with the spiritual world, they required powerful imaginations to perceive the problems, sharp brains to conceive the solutions, and skilled hands to create the instruments to record them.

These men set out to create a workable methodology, but like all natural scientists, like all of us in fact, they had to work within the most arbitrary of constraints.

Our present calendar is entirely unsatisfactory. With the fashion of rationalization and decimals it is surprising that we should put up with a year of 365.2422166 days, divided into unequal months adding an hour here and taking it away there, in what seems a hugely undisciplined fashion. The only reason July and August have thirty-one days is because the Emperor Augustus Caesar wished it. In his arrogance he decreed that the months which in future would bear his name and that of his great uncle Julius should contain the maximum number of thirty-one days. Why this ancient edict should still have relevance today is a mystery. Twelve months of thirty days each and a welcome and hard-earned national holiday to use up the residue would make everyone's lives simple, and the lives of

129

scientists, tax inspectors and bank managers in particular a bed of roses.

The Babylonians had the good sense to enforce just such a division and their splitting of the year into 360 days led to the 360-degree circle, as their twelve-monthly cycle led to the twelve signs of the zodiac.

With such a sensible system, it was possible to devise a sundial which would measure not just the time of year and the time of day but the direction of the wind and much else besides. Such a sundial is the tower of the winds, or Horologian, built by Andronikos, and no more than a short walk from the Pantheaon. The Horologian is octagonal with one face given over to each of the eight winds. No one face can show all the hours of the day all the days of the year; but together they ensure that this astonishing structure is not just a calendar, not just a clock and not just a wind-vane, but a mystical linking of gods and men, of the spiritual and natural worlds.

Perhaps Andronikos, the architect of the weather, was the first great meteorologist. But there are a hundred more, without whom we would have no such thing as meteorology. Of the hundred, there are a few inductive philosophers, several of whose specific contribution to the science is of sufficient importance for them to merit inclusion, a greater number of theorists, as well as those who contrived experiments and designed instruments with which to carry them out.

The chapter may safely be skipped by any whose interest in the weather is casual, but even they may find it useful for winning bets in pubs. Those intrigued by such an array of dedication and talent may discover more details in the bio-graphical dictionaries, or in the writings of these great men. Their works live after them.

490 BC; Empedocles introduced the idea of the four elements, concluding that all natural phenomena could be explained by different compounds of earth, air, fire and water. He flung

himself into the volcanic crater of Mount Etna to convince his followers of his immortality.

c.460–*c*.377 BC; Hippocrates wrote a treatise 'Prognostics: Airs, Waters and Places', in which he argued that climate is pre-eminent in forming the lifestyle and personalities of men and women just as diet is responsible for health. Aristotle called him 'the Great Physician', but added that he was short in stature.

384–322 BC; Aristotle. His *Meteorologica* is the earliest examination of the subject and has been enormously influential. The word meteorology derives from his work. In it he is critical of his predecessors (including Empedocles and Hippocrates) and deals with all physical matters, from the causes of shooting stars to the formation of cloud, from dew and hoarfrost to hail, from the classification of winds to a theory of thunder and lightning. Wonderfully detailed, delightfully observed, always to the point.

c.372–287 BC; Theophrastus of Eresus, a pupil of Aristotle and his literary executor. He wrote one treatise 'On Winds' and another 'On the Signs of Rain, Winds, Storms and Fair Weather'. It was his proposal that winds coming from the sea were more likely to bring rain and that clouds passing over mountains more likely to deposit it.

c.315–245 BC; Aratus of Soli, a Greek physician, astronomer and poet. His major works were his 'Book of Signs and Phaenomena', a didactic poem in hexameters, 400 lines of which are devoted to weather lore. An example:

'When in autumn wasps collect in many groups in the evening one may be sure that the following winter will be cold in proportion to the extent and closeness of the groups.'

Working 1337–44 AD; the Rev. William Mede. The first man – so far as we know – to keep a daily weather record over seven years in Oxford and in Driby, Lincs, of which parish he was the vicar.

1452–1519; Leonardo da Vinci. Amongst his numerous designs was one for an early anemometer, later developed by Robert Hooke (q.v.).

1527–1608; John Dee, a Fellow of the Royal Society, recorded weather observations for seven years, and became so accurate a forecaster he was branded as a witch. Astrologer to Mary Tudor and to Elizabeth I, he also gave navigational advice to explorers making for the New World.

1564–1642; Galileo Galilei invented the thermometer soon after becoming a professor at Padua. Besides the thermometer he also discovered the theory of pendulums, the acceleration of gravity, the telescope and, consequently, Jupiter's satellites. But he did *not* drop weights from the Leaning Tower of Pisa.

1571–1630; Johannes Kepler, a celebrated philosopher and astrologer, proposed the movement of the solar system based on ellipses (not circles like Copernicus). He also insisted on the influence of the moon over the tides and founded modern optics by postulating the ray theory of light to explain vision.

Working 1627; Joseph Furtenbach, a mathematician from Ulm, proved that the earth rotates (as Copernicus proposed and Galileo declared) by firing a cannon vertically into the air, then sitting on the mouth of the cannon.

1596–1650; René Descartes, alerted by the political problems which Galileo had faced, migrated to Holland to publish his principal works, thence at Queen Christina's insistence, to Stockholm. To Descartes we owe the graph without which meteorologists would be miserable.

1602–86; Otto von Guericke used a glass tube to construct a thirty-four-foot glass barometer with which he predicted a violent storm. The prediction was famously fulfilled but his barometer broke. It was he too who created an airtight sphere from which all the air was pumped out. It then took sixteen horses to pull the two halves of the sphere apart. He also invented the first electrical generator.

1608–47; Evangelista Torricelli. Galileo's amanuensis discovered the principles of the mercury barometer and improved both the telescope and microscope.

1620–84; Edme Mariotte, one of the earliest members of France's Academy of Sciences, independently discovered that the volume of a gas varies inversely with the pressure. Boyle had made the same discovery in Oxford.

1623–62; Blaise Pascal, author of the *Pensées*, sent his brother up the Puy-de-Dome mountain carrying a mercury barometer. As he ascended the mercury level fell, from which experiment he produced Pascal's Law of Pressure. He also invented the digital calculator.

1627–91; Robert Boyle, Irishman, Etonian, undertook numerous experiments in Oxford, notably discovering the relation of volume to pressure, thereafter known as Boyle's Law.

1629–98; Christiaan Huygens propounded the wave theory of light, and invented a new system for grinding and polishing lenses, discovering the precise shape of the rings of Saturn with his improved telescope.

1632–1723; Christopher Wren designed the first rain-collector that emptied itself as soon as it was full up. He founded the Royal Society.

1635–1703; Robert Hooke was Boyle's assistant. Among his inventions were 'thirty several ways of flying', the wheel barometer (with the familiar legends – rain, changeable, fair, etc. – which we still find on barometers) and, using Leonardo's sketches, the first anemometer, or wind-measurer. Hooke's barometer graduations were engraved on instruments by the great George Sinclair.

1642–1727; Sir Isaac Newton. In his *Principia* he established the laws of gravitational attraction, with their relevance to the moon and tides. He also contrived a temperature scale and a vast amount of innovative mathematics and physics. As a boy he tried to determine the speed of the wind in the great storm of 1658 by jumping with the wind, then against it.

1647–1712; Denis Papin assisted Huygens with his air-pump and later worked with Robert Boyle. He became 'temporary curator of experiments at the Royal Society' and died in obscurity. He is best remembered for his 'digester', later known as a pressure cooker, a means of heating water beyond boiling point.

1625–1715; William Dampier, piratical sea captain whose book *A Voyage Round the World* (1697) inspired Defoe to write *Gulliver's Travels*. Dampier's book contained splendid and valuable observations on winds, tides and currents.

1686–1736; Daniel Gabriel Fahrenheit, originally from Danzig, besides improving hygrometers and thermometers, invented the scale of temperature which runs from 32°F (melting point of ice to 212°F (boiling point of water at sea level).

1701–44; Anders Celsius, Swedish astronomer, who published his observations on the Aurora Borealis, among other matters. In 1742 he offered his temperature scale to the Swedish Academy of Sciences. Read downwards from 100 as the melting point of ice to 0 as the boiling point of water. A confused public demanded the reverse and got its way. He built the Uppsala Observatory from which he viewed the Aurora Borealis.

1706–90; Benjamin Franklin flew a kite into a severe thunderstorm. The lightning travelled down a damp thread and jumped to a metal key. Franklin concluded that static electricity is the same as lightning and developed the lightning conductor. He also wrote extensively on other meteorological matters, such as earthquakes, waterspouts and whirlwinds. A brilliant, acclaimed, but sententious man.

1726–97; James Hutton, from Edinburgh, gave us the wet and dry bulb thermometer and published an invaluable paper in 1784 on the 'Theory of Rain'.

1727–1817; Jean André Deluc was a Swiss businessman and politician who emigrated to England in 1773 and became Queen Charlotte's reader. As a meteorologist he concerned himself with humidity and evaporations; he invented a new hygrometer; codified rules for estimating heights with a barometer and discovered the 'dry pole' or electric column.

1733–1812; Richard Kirwan was brought up by a Jesuit, left the order, married, and was arrested on his wedding day for his wife's debts. A Fellow of the Royal Society and a Copley medallist he studied the temperatures of different latitudes, working towards an explanation of prevailing winds. He returned to Ireland in 1787 and 'was consulted as a weather prophet by half the farmers of Ireland'.

1736–1813; Joseph Louis Lagrange spent the Revolutionary years in Paris and survived them. A mathematician, he advanced theories concerning planetary perturbation and the stability of the solar system.

1738–1822; Sir William Herschel, originally a musician in Hanover, was sent to be an organist at Bath. Fascinated by astronomy, and unable to afford a telescope, he built one. Herschel discovered Uranus, was the first to detect the existence of the binary stars, announced that gravity was operative in outer space and built a mighty reflecting telescope of a focal length of forty feet in 1789, by which time he was private astronomer to the king.

1740–99; Horace Benedict de Sausssure at the charming age of twenty was appointed to the Chair of Philosophy at Geneva. At the age of forty-seven he climbed Mont Blanc. As a geologist he was only too aware of the inadequacies of the instruments available to him. He perfected a thermometer to measure deep water, as well as hygrometers, ludiometers, electrometers, anemometers, cyanometers and diaphano-meters. I could tell you what these are, but I won't.

1743–94; Antoine Laurent Laroisier, a natural scientist and born administrator, wrote papers on thunder and the Aurora Borealis. A member of the 'farmers general', he was regarded as untrustworthy and tragically guillotined with twenty-seven other intellectuals.

1744–1829; Jean Baptiste Lamarck, a Darwinian from Picardy, was a pioneer in weather-mapping. He published an annual series of meteorological surveys from 1800 to 1816, when Napoleon told him to stick to Natural History. In 1802 he listed five types of clouds which he enlarged to twelve categories in 1805.

1749–1827; Pierre Simon Laplace was known as the Newton of France. His eminent career in science included meteorological subjects, and in *Méchanique Céleste* he wrote on the baro-metrical determination of height. He was president of the improbable-sounding Bureau of Longitudes, and helped organize the decimal system.

1766–1832; Sir John Leslie came from Fife, but travelled exten-sively as tutor to young Americans. A natural historian, mathematician and physicist, he originated Leslie's cube – for radiation experiments – a dry-and-wet-bulb hygrometer and a differential air thermometer.

1766–1844; John Dalton, a Quaker and distinguished chemist and physicist, began a meteorological journal in March 1787, the night of a remarkable aurora, and maintained it for the rest of his life. His atomic theory made him famous, but his aurora and condensation studies are almost as significant. According to Sir Napier Shaw (to whose scholarship I owe so much) Dalton 'never had time to marry'.

1772–1864; Like Dalton, Luke Howard was a Quaker. His principal claim to fame comes from his classification of clouds (more scientific than Lamarck). He also kept a meteorological register from 1830 of the weather in Tottenham, and published his *Barometrigraphia*, concerning his self-recording barograph or 'Barometer Clock'. He perceived an eighteen-year cycle in British weather.

1773–1829; Thomas Tong was yet another Quaker whose celebrated series of lectures at the Royal Institution in 1807 expounded a new technique for estimating the size of particles in a cloud by measuring the diameter of its coronal rays. Savaged by Lord Brougham in the *Edinburgh Review* he published a pamphlet in his own defence but only sold one copy. Hounded out of meteorology he took up Egyptology 'in which also he was disappointed'.

1774–1862; Jean Baptiste Biot accompanied Guy-Lussac (q.v.) on a scientifically motivated balloon ascent. Biot's work on the polarization of light shines like a beacon.

1774–1857; Rear Admiral Sir Francis Beaufort devised his Beaufort Scale of wind force in 1806, based on the progress of a well-maintained man of war. In a revised form it is still in use today; he also devised the Beaufort notation for weather. A master of brevity he surveyed the Greek archipelagi and rounded up Levantine pirates in an active and distinguished life.

1777–1834; Johann Gauss, a professor of mathematics at Hanover, invented a new means of measuring planetary orbits. He also invented the helestrope, founded a Magnetic Association, wrote on probability, and many other learned subjects. The unit of magnetic force is named after him.

1777–1834; Heinrich Brandes constructed a series of daily weather charts, and in 1820 conceived the idea of collating weather observations from all over the country onto a single map.

1778–1850; Louis Guy-Lussac ascended twice in a balloon to measure the temperature and moisture of the air and the strength of terrestrial magnetism. A joint memoir with von Humboldt to the French Academy of Sciences contained the first assertion that water was formed of two parts hydrogen and one part oxygen.

c.1778–1840; Clement Descombes determined the absolute zero of temperature and proved that the quality of heat contained in a given weight of vapour is constant for all temperatures and pressures, if the space is saturated within the vapour.

1781–1868; William Redfield, America's pioneer meteorologist, collated observations of West Indian hurricanes over ten years and constructed a series of synoptic charts, identifying the origins of these storms, their usual routes, the rotations within them, and such matters. After observing the Massachusetts storm of 1821 he concluded that storms in the northern hemisphere swirl in an anti-clockwise direction unlike those south of the Equator.

1781–1868; Sir David Brewster, a Scot, wrote Newton's biography and in 1820 drew attention to the geographical pole and 'the poles of greatest cold'. He persuaded the English to adopt the Fresnel lightweight lens for use in lighthouses.

1785–1860; James Pollard Espy, inspired by the work of Dalton (q.v.) and Daniell (q.v.), turned from the classics to meteorology, specializing in thunderstorms and suchlike phenomena. He gave the first essentially correct explanation of the thermodynamics of cloud formation. He travelled from the Franklin Institute to Europe to promulgate his theories. John Quincy Adams wrote: 'The man is methodically monomaniac and the dimensions of his organs of self-esteem have been swollen to the size of a goitre by a report of the committee of the National Institute of France endorsing all of his crack-brained discoveries in Meteorology'. One of his plans was to burn timber to induce rain in drought-ridden areas.

1788–1883; Sir Edward Sabine – born in Dublin – lived ninety-five years, and filled those years with an energetic commitment to meteorology. He explored the Arctic, worked on pendulums, undertook a magnetic survey of Britain, initiated observation posts in many of the colonies, and was President of the Royal Society, 1861–71.

1790–1845; John Daniell, originally a sugar-refiner, became a meteorologist at the age of twenty-three. He invented both the Daniell Cell and the Daniell Hygrometer for the determination of the dew-point. He continued Luke Howard's (q.v.) work on the climate of London and was awarded the Horticultural Society's medal for a paper on greenhouse humidity.

1791–1867; Michael Faraday's *Experimental Researches in Electricity* (1850) suggested that it was the magnetic force contained within currents of wind which causes the movements of storm centres. Faraday's Motor, which used direct current only, might well be applied to cloud masses and would explain their powerful rotations. Not specifically a meteorologist, and without a formal education, Faraday's work has been of great service to meteorology. Incidentally, it was his portrait which overhung Albert Einstein's desk.

1791–1868; Claude-Servais Pouillet was a French physicist, with expertise in solar heat and the temperature of space. Concerned primarily with clouds, he devised a photographic technique for determining their height.

b.1791 Major General William Reid was author of *The Progress of the Development of the Law of Storms and of the Variable Winds* (London, 1849). He gave rules by which sailors could hope to avoid the worst of hurricanes, and established an early warning system in Barbados and a self-recording barometer in Bridgetown.

1792–1871; Sir John Herschel, son of the famous astronomer, Sir William Herschel (q.v.), continued his father's work in optics and astronomy. However, he made at least one valuable contribution to meteorology, suggesting that there could be benefits to be derived from taking meteorological observations simultaneously at different posts.

1792–?; John Robinson, an Irish astronomer and physicist, developed Robert Hooke's q.v. ideas for measuring the wind and developed the first cup anemometer with several cups pivoting on a vertical spindle. The faster they revolve, the stronger the wind.

1792–1843; Gustave Coriolis wrote a scientific paper in 1835 with an unrepeatable French title; but the burden of his work was that the swirls of storms received their direction as a result of the earth's rotation. The 'Coriolis Force', as it has come to be called, has direct influence on such associated matters as ocean currents and the corrections which long-range bombers need to make when targeting their bombs.

b.1797; Henry Piddington inherited William Reid's q.v. investigative fervour and wrote: *The Sailor's Horn-book for the Laws of Storms in all parts of the World* (London and Edinburgh, 1855). He first coined the word 'Cyclone', Greek for the coils of a snake. ('Typhoon', incidentally, derives from the Chinese Ta-Feng, meaning violent winds.)

1801–67; Ludwig Kamtz was a farmer's son from Pomerania who became by turns a lawyer, a classicist, and a mathematical philosopher. Inspired by the writings of Jean Baptiste Biot (q.v.) and overwhelmed with the power of a sudden Baltic storm, he produced his *Lehrbuch der Meteorologie* in three volumes (1831–6). He also instigated a splendid periodical, his *Reportorium Für Meteorologie*. A learned comment on his handbook: 'There is hardly a single work anywhere on physical geography or climatology that is worth noting which has appeared in the course of the last forty years and has not been based more or less on Kamtz's work.'

b. 1803; Heinrich Dove, from Silesia, published a book *The Law of Storms* which led to him being called 'the founder of the entire superstructure of accurate climatological knowledge'. He produced monthly maps of isotherms of the globe, and theorized that the changing weather patterns in the temperate zones resulted from the conflict between the equatorial current of the atmosphere and the polar currents.

1805–65; Admiral Robert Fitzroy had such an eventful life that I am tempted to turn him into the hero of a musical. He was captain of the Beagle when Darwin made his historic voyage. Appointed Governor of New Zealand, he defended the rights of the Maoris with such fervour that the English settlers demanded that he be replaced. Promoted to Admiral, he was entrusted with the task of developing a weather warning system as Head of the new Meteorological Department of the Board of Trade. He quickly produced a mercury barometer, ideal for use at sea, with detailed instructions as to its use. The first public weather forecasts were issued to the Press in July 1861. The Royal Society bitterly opposed these, questioning their scientific accuracy, and the Admiral was deeply upset, as a fundamentalist, at the use to which Darwin was putting his observations. On 30 April 1865, Fitzroy cut his throat with a razor.

1806–73; After Mathew Maury, an American naval officer, had met with a serious accident, he turned to supplying log books and maritime and meteorological observations to ships' captains. He worked tirelessly towards international cooperation and published *The Physical Geography of the Sea* in 1855 in London and the following year in New York. During the Civil War he invented an electric torpedo.

1811–89; Elias Loomis was a Yale professor who researched into the movement of typhoons, storms and hurricanes, concluding that in the upper air above the United States there is a powerful air current blowing from west to east. His detailed description of how depressions form in these prevailing winds was a development of Espy's (q.v.) theory. He called for the establishment of regular weather charts for the US.

1817–90; Christophorus Buys Ballot was a Dutch professor of physics who formulated a law in 1858 that winds are perpendicular to their lines of barometric slope. For six years prior to this he had been compiling daily weather maps and publishing them in a yearbook. In 1860, he propounded the rule that if you stand with your back to the wind, low pressure will be on your left (the reverse applies in the Southern Hemisphere). Buys-Ballot, it can be claimed, was the first person to introduce a daily weather forecast. Telegrams from six observation posts were distributed to shipping posts. In 1868 this energetic man introduced his aeroclinoscope, which indicated the position of the centre of a depression, and its gradient.

1822–85; John Francis Campbell of Islay devised the first instrument for recording the duration of sunshine. It came to be called a heliograph. Campbell's device was a hemisphere of wood with a glass sphere mounted centrally. The rays of the sun would clear the wood through the glass. The primitive heliograph was further developed by . . .

1819–1902;. . . Sir George Stokes in 1879. He added several refinements including a graduated card to record the day-to-day sunshine record. He also formulated Stokes's Law of Hydrodynamics and Stokes's Law of Fluorescence.

n.d.; John Glaisher of the Greenwich Royal Observatory made a series of historic balloon ascents to measure temperature and atmospheric depression for the British Association. These continued the brave work initiated by John Welsh, the Observatory's Superintendent. In 1862, he rose to 11,500 metres, compared to about 7,000 metres reached by Welsh. He was almost asphyxiated and had to pull the descent valve's release with his teeth. These balloon descents ended with the tragic death of Walter Powell MP who was carried out to sea after failing to land on the Bridport sands.

n.d.; James Croll, a Scot who first identified that the earth's orbit is by no means regular and that its irregularities have a significant effect on the climate.

1883–1964; Victor Hess, a Viennese physicist, anxious to solve the mystery of why the sky should be electrically charged while the earth remains negative, proved that radiation enters the atmosphere from space. His discovery enlarged the scope of modern physics and his conclusion that it was due to cosmic rays ionizing the earth's atmosphere, won him the Nobel Prize in 1936.

d. 1918; Joseph Nowack should perhaps not feature in this hall of fame because it is probable that he was a fraud. He applied for a patent in 1887 for a 'weather-plant' which could accurately forecast the weather. The plant (Abrus Precaforius) could – apparently – anticipate most weather conditions, and Mr Nowack was invited to give demonstrations at Kew. His claims became more and more extreme until 1908, when he fell silent and died ten years later.

1862–1951; Wilhelm Bjerknes and his brother Jacob were Scandinavians who invented dynamic meteorology and hydrography. This seems to mean the movements of air and water masses. Their novel theory was that storms were produced when eddies developed along the fronts between colliding air masses. The eddies became subject to the Coriolis (q.v.) force, and developed into storms.

1879–1958; Milutin Milankovitch, a Serb, further developed the theories of James Croll (q.v.) about the irregularity of the earth's orbit. He gave his name to the Milankovitch Wobbles, from which spring the Milankovitch Cycles of 23,000, 41,000 and 100,000 years.

n.d.; Lewis Richardson's book, *Weather Prediction by Numerical Process*, was a novel approach (in 1922) to an ancient science. He predicted a weather factory of 64,000 workers processing the information from 64,000 control points which might be able to forecast the weather accurately before it had a chance to change. 'But that is a dream', he added. With the speed of computers and the accuracy of weather satellite observations, his dream seems no longer so dreamlike.

n.d.; George Cowling is acknowledged to be the first British Television weatherman. He set off at 5 am every morning from the Air Ministry to the Shepherd's Bush studios of the BBC with his meteorological chart for the day; on top of his civil service salary he received an appearance fee of ten shillings.

Edward Lorenz (b.1917) a meteorologist at the MIT, was the first to progamme weather patterns onto his (primitive) computer. The wide divergencies between apparently similar pro-grammes led him to conclude that tiny and immeasurable changes at the centre of developing weather systems must be responsible.

And finally, although he was not a meteorologist it would be foolish to leave out . . .

Roy C. Sullivan, the only person to survive being struck by lightning seven times. He lost his big toenail in 1942, his eyebrows in 1969, and had his hair set on fire twice. The other times he suffered slight burns.

Bibliography

The mother and father of them all is the *Manual of Meteorology* by Sir Napier Shaw (Cambridge University Press, 1926). This massive work in four volumes is essential reading for anyone seriously concerned in the study of meteorology. As the author charmingly remarks in his preface:

'The four volumes which this work is intended to comprise are the expensive embodiment of a personal feeling that, for the community as a whole, there is nothing so extravagantly expensive as ignorance, however cheap it may be for any particular section of it.' Volume 1 which deals with *Meteorology in History* (OUP, 1926) and Volume 2 with *Comparative Meteorology* (OUP, 1927) may be read with interest and pleasure by any interested reader. Volumes 3 and 4 are increasingly technical.

Also technical but scholastically respectable is Dr R. C. Sutcliffe's *Meteorology for Aviators* which formed the substantial basis for the *Handbook of Aviation Meteorology* by A. F. Crossley and others (HMSO, 1960). This is especially useful on matters relating to clouds and cloud cover, but it is not light reading! *A Century of London Weather* by W. A. L. Marshall (HMSO, 1952) continued through many updates and revisions, but is statistically invaluable.

Quite a useful layman's survey is contained in *The Weather of Britain* by Robin Stirling (Faber, 1982) and an attractive large format volume is *The Great British Obsession* by Francis Wilson (Jarrold, 1990). The handsome illustrations are not matched by a basic text. *British Weather* by Stephen Bone (Collins, 1946, in the Britain in Pictures series) is a delightful essay but of more interest to the bibliophile than the meteorologist. *Weather Watch* (Fourth Estate, 1990) is taken from Dick File's *Guardian* column. It is pedagogic and dull but contains much useful information.

Ideal for children is *The Usborne Book of Weather Facts* by Anita Ganeri (Usborne, 1987). It presents weather facts and comparisons in a highly readable way and has the approval of the London Weather Centre, which keeps a permanent library of books for sale. *Freak Weather* by Graham J. McEwan (Robert Hale, 1991) is anecdotal but not without interest. *The Great Drought of 1976* by Evelyn Cox (Hutchinson, 1978) is a personal account of the drought in Herefordshire, beautifully observed and written.

For international weather *The World Weather Guide* by E. A. Pearce and C. G. Smith (Hutchinson, 1984 and 1990) is a formidable work of statistical scholarship, while *The Weather Companion* by Gary Lockhart (John Wiley and Sons, New York, 1988) is chatty and engaging. *The Greenhouse Effect* by Stewart Boyle and John Ardill (New English Library, 1989) is useful for reference but *Turning Up The Heat* by Fred Pearce (Bodley Head, 1989) is the essential book for conscientious environmentalists.

Appendix I

Conversion Table Celsius to Fahrenheit

C	F	C	F	C	F	C	F
50	122	25	77	0	32	−25	−13
49	120.2	24	75.2	− 1	30.2	−26	−14.8
48	118.4	23	73.4	− 2	28.4	−27	−16.6
47	116.6	22	71.6	− 3	26.6	−28	−18.4
46	114.8	21	69.8	− 4	24.8	−29	−20.2
45	113	20	68	− 5	23	−30	−22
44	111.2	19	66.2	− 6	21.2	−31	−23.8
43	109.4	18	64.4	− 7	19.4	−32	−25.6
42	107.6	17	62.6	− 8	17.6	−33	−27.4
41	105.8	16	60.8	− 9	15.8	−34	−29.2
40	104	15	59	−10	14	−35	−31
39	102.2	14	57.2	−11	12.2	−36	−32.8
38	100.4	13	55.4	−12	10.4	−37	−34.6
37	98.6	12	53.6	−13	8.6	−38	−36.4
36	96.8	11	51.8	−14	6.8	−39	−38.2
35	95	10	50	−15	5	−40	−40
34	93.2	9	48.2	−16	3.2	−41	−41.8
33	91.4	8	46.4	−17	1.4	−42	−43.6
32	89.6	7	44.6	−18	−0.4	−43	−45.4
31	87.8	6	42.8	−19	−2.2	−44	−47.2
30	86	5	41	−20	−4	−45	−49
29	84.2	4	39.2	−21	−5.8	−46	−50.8
28	82.4	3	37.4	−22	−7.6	−47	−52.6
27	80.6	2	35.6	−23	−9.4	−48	−54.4
26	78.8	1	33.8	−24	−11.2	−49	−56.2

Appendix II

Comparison Table

1 m.p.h. = 0.8684 knots	1 knot = 1.152 m.p.h.
5 m.p.h. = 4.342	5 knots = 5.76 m.p.h.
10 m.p.h. = 8.684	10 knots = 11.52 m.p.h.
15 m.p.h. = 13.026	15 knots = 17.28 m.p.h.
20 m.p.h. = 17.368	20 knots = 23.04 m.p.h.
25 m.p.h. = 21.71	25 knots = 28.80 m.p.h.
30 m.p.h. = 26.052	30 knots = 34.56 m.p.h.
35 m.p.h. = 30.394	35 knots = 40.32 m.p.h.
40 m.p.h. = 34.736	40 knots = 46.08 m.p.h.
50 m.p.h. = 43.42	50 knots = 57.60 m.p.h.
60 m.p.h. = 52.104	60 knots = 69.12 m.p.h.
70 m.p.h. = 60.788	70 knots = 80.64 m.p.h.
80 m.p.h. = 69.472	80 knots = 92.16 m.p.h.
90 m.p.h. = 78.156	90 knots = 103.68 m.p.h.
100 m.p.h. = 86.84	100 knots = 115.20 m.p.h.
110 m.p.h. = 95.524	110 knots = 126.72 m.p.h.
120 m.p.h. = 104.208	120 knots = 138.24 m.p.h.
130 m.p.h. = 112.892	130 knots = 149.76 m.p.h.
140 m.p.h. = 121.576	140 knots = 161.28 m.p.h.
150 m.p.h. = 130.26	150 knots = 172.80 m.p.h.
160 m.p.h. = 138.944	160 knots = 184.32 m.p.h.
170 m.p.h. = 147.628	170 knots = 195.84 m.p.h.
180 m.p.h. = 156.312	180 knots = 207.36 m.p.h.
190 m.p.h. = 164.996	190 knots = 218.88 m.p.h.
200 m.p.h. = 173.68	200 knots = 230.40 m.p.h.

Appendix III

There are now so many initials, acronyms and mnemonics in the international world of weather-watching that I thought a short glossary might be of value.

ATS 1 – The first geostationary weather satellite, followed by the American GOES series, and Europe's METEOSATS.

AVHRR – Advanced Very High Resolution Radiometer. This is the main imager on board the TIROS – N and has three infra red and two conventional channels.

BMRC – Bureau of Meteorology Research Centre (Australian).

CFC – Chlorofluorocarbons. Not only the villains of the piece, but devilish to spell.

CNES – the French Space Agency.

COSMOS – Russian satellites, later to become known as METEORS.

DOGGIE – a charming acronym for Deep Ocean Geological and Geophysical Instrument Explorer. An eight-metre-long planned robot which will take an acoustic picture of the sea bed, while acting as a satellite to a mother ship.

DOLPHIN – an ingenious acronym for the Deep Ocean Long Path Hydrographic Instrument. An underwater robot to monitor the Atlantic.

ENMOD – A UN Convention outlawing Environmental Modification, signed in Geneva in 1977.

ECMWS – European Centre for Medium-Range Weather Forecasts, based at Shinfield Park near Reading.

ENSO – El Nino Southern Oscillation – a convenient acronym for weather changes caused by ocean currents in the south Pacific.

ERS 1 – A European programme to monitor the Earth's environment from space. Blasted off in April 1991.

ERS 2 – A satellite which will bridge the gap between two European observation projects and ameliorate exchange of climatic information. Due to be launched in April 1994 at a projected cost of £297 million.

ESA – European Space Agency.

ESSA – Environmental Science Services Administration.

FENGYUN – the Chinese weather satellite.

FRONTIERS – Forecasting Rain Optimized Using New Techniques of Interactively Enhanced Radar and Satellite Data. A section within the Centre for Climate Prediction and Research at Bracknell, it wins the prize for the clumsiest acronym.

GARP – Global Atmospheric Research Programme, which acts as a sort of traffic cop to weather satellites.

GEO – Geostationary Orbit. Not changing its position *vis à vis* the movement of the earth. As in MOP 1.

GISS – Goddard Institute for Space Studies, New York.

GMS – Geostationary Meteorological Satellite. Japanese.

GOMS – Geostationary Operational Meteorological Satellite. Russian and would have been spin-stabilized but never became operational.

GOES – American weather satellites launched from 1975 onwards. Measure solar activity, and information from ocean buoys, river gauges, etc.

GOFS – Global Ocean Flux Study.

GRID – Global Resource Information Database, produced by UNEP.

IGBP – International Geosphere-Biosphere Project.

INSAT – India's weather satellite which ceased operations in 1988.

IPCC – Intergovernmental Panel on Climate Change.

ITOS – An improved TIROS. Six launched between 1969 and 1976.

LAWS – Laser Atmospheric Wind Sounder.

MEOSTATS – European Meteorological Satellites.

MESA – Maximum Entropy Spectrum Analysis, a technique developed by Robert Currie of NASA to chart fluctuations in the earth's axis.

METEORS – More sophisticated versions of COSMOS satellites.

METEOSAT – Europe's contribution to the WWW. Launched for the European Space Agency, the first one in 1977.

MOP 1 – Europe's first operational meteorological satellite, launched on the Ariane V29 rocket and now known as MEOSTAT 4 in orbit.

NASA – National Aeronautics and Space Administration.

NCAR – National Center for Atmospheric Research (American).

NEXRAD – from NEXt generation RADar. Instruments using doppler radar which can assess the direction and speed of the wind.

NIMBUS – A series of weather satellites first launched in 1964.

NOAA – National Oceanographic and Atmospheric Administration. It succeeded ESSA. Its satellites now carry the solar backscatter instruments to measure ozone distribution, and the Budget Experiment which charts radiation changes in the atmosphere.

RADARSAT – A proposed Canadian satellite of great sophistication to be launched – supposedly – in 1994 at a cost projected to be £750 million.

SEASAT – A satellite launched in 1978, and active for only three months, it provided useful data on marine conditions.

SMS – The Synchronous Meteorological Satellite from Ford Aerospace.

SPOT – The French optical satellite. It had the limitation of so many weather satellites that it couldn't 'see through' cloud cover.

SST – Sea Surface Temperature.

TIROS – Television/Infra-Red Observation Satellite. Ten of these were launched between 1960 and 1965.

TOGA – Tropical Ocean-Global Atmosphere.

TOS – A TIROS operational system organized by ESSA, which despatched nine satellites between 1966 and 1969.

TOVS – The TIROS Operational Vertical Sounder provides temperature charts of the earth's surface, water vapour readings from the atmosphere, and ozone readings.

UNEP – United Nations Environment Programme.

WMAB – Weather Modification Advisory Board. An American organization which means what it says.

WMO – World Meteorological Organization, an off-shoot of the United Nations.

WOCE – World Ocean Circulation Experiment.

WWW – the World Weather Watch programme initiated by the United Nations.

Index

155

Bruton, record day's rainfall, 77
Bryson, Reid, 110
Bucharest, 97
Bushey Park, 6
Buxton, 84
Buys Ballot, Christophorus, 142
Byron, Lord, 16

Cairngorms, 84
calendar, 129–30
Campbell, John Francis, 142
Campbell-Stokes Sunshine
  Recorder, 55
Canada: climate control survey,
  104–5; greenhouse gas, 118, 119
Canterbury, 55
carbon dioxide, levels in
  atmosphere, 109–10, 114, 117
Celsius, Anders, 134
Central Forecasting Office, 30, 31
Centre for Crop Circle Studies, 91
Century of London Weather, A
  (Marshall), 54
CEPS (Circles Effect Phenomena), 89,
  92
CFCS (chlorofluorocarbons), 118, 119
Charles Darwin, (research ship), 115
Charlton, Suzanne, 23, 24
Cheeseford Head, 89
Cheltenham, 53
Chernobyl, 69
Chichester Cathedral, 6
Chikwana, Elephigio, 49
China, greenhouse gas, 118
Choy, Chris, 26
Christmas, 38, 41; snow at, 85, 87
Christy, John, 112
Churchill, Sir Winston, 23
Civil Aviation Authority, 28
Clandon House, 6
Clean Air Act (1956), 66, 67, 68, 70
Cleethorpes, 61
climate: fluctuations, 12–14, 55–60;
  extremes, 17, 55, 57, 59, 62, 73–4,
  80–83; attempts to control, 50,
  102–6; research, 108–21, 122–8,
clothing, during heat waves, 20–22
clouds, 114; seeding, 103, 104, 105
Coffeyville (Kansas), 93
Colchester, 84
Colombia, greenhouse gas, 118
Colorado Springs, 49

communication systems, 149–53
computers: in forecasting, 23, 26, 28,
  29, 30; lightning and, 47
Conny, Dr Robert, 95
Conrad, Joseph, 1
Corbyn, Piers, 26–7
Coriolis, Gustave, 140
Cornwall, 18; 1891 snowfall, 85
Cowling, George, 144
Cranstead, 95
Cray YMP 832 Computer, 30
Croll, James, 113, 143, 144
crop circles, 88–92
Crowhurst, Donald, 80
Cuba, 103
Culham Lightning Studies Unit, 49
Cumulus weather ship, 30–31
cyclones, 31, 140

Dallas (Texas), 93
Dalton, John, 136, 138
Dampier, William, 134
Daniell, John, 138, 139
Dartcom, 28
Dartmoor, 86
Database, 27
Davies, Paul, 48
De la Mare, Walter, 8
Deacon Laboratory, 31
Dee, John, 132
Defoe, Daniel, 5, 134
Dell 210 computer, 27
Deluc, Jean André, 135
Denness, Dr Bruce, 116
depressions, 30, 33, 74
Descartes, René, 132
Descombes, Clement, 138
Devon, 1891 snowfall, 85
Dijkhuis, Geert, 48
DOGGIE (Deep Ocean Geological and
  Geophysical Instrumented
  Explorer), 31
DOLPHIN (Deep Ocean Long Path
  Hydrographic Instruments), 31
Doncaster, 73
Dove, Heinrich, 141
droughts, 19–20, 56–62, 114;
  definition, 60; effects, 61–2
Dublin, smog, 68
dust-devils, 61, 89, 90, 95, 96

earth-tremors, 62